CRYSTALS:

*Their Role
in Nature
and
in Science*

ACADEMIC PAPERBACKS*

BIOLOGY

Edited by ALVIN NASON

Design and Function at the Threshold of Life: The Viruses
    HEINZ FRAENKEL-CONRAT
Time, Cells, and Aging BERNARD L. STREHLER
Isotopes in Biology GEORGE WOLF
Life: Its Nature, Origin, and Development A. I. OPARIN

MATHEMATICS

Edited by W. MAGNUS and A. SHENITZER

Finite Permutation Groups HELMUT WIELANDT
Introduction to p-Adic Numbers and Valuation Theory
    GEORGE BACHMAN
Quadratic Forms and Matrices N. V. YEFIMOV
Elements of Abstract Harmonic Analysis
    GEORGE BACHMAN
Noneuclidean Geometry HERBERT MESCHKOWSKI

PHYSICS

Edited by D. ALLAN BROMLEY

Elementary Dynamics of Particles H. W. HARKNESS
Elementary Plane Rigid Dynamics H. W. HARKNESS
Crystals: Their Role in Nature and in Science CHARLES BUNN
Potential Barriers in Semiconductors B. R. GOSSICK
Mössbauer Effect: Principles and Applications
    GUNTHER K. WERTHEIM

* Most of these volumes are also available in a cloth bound
edition.

CRYSTALS:

Their Role in Nature and in Science

by

Charles Bunn

The Royal Institution
London, England

Formerly of Imperial Chemical Industries

ACADEMIC PRESS • NEW YORK and LONDON

ACADEMIC PRESS INC.
111 Fifth Avenue, New York, New York 10003

United Kingdom Edition published by
ACADEMIC PRESS INC. (LONDON) LTD.
Berkeley Square House, London W.1

LIBRARY OF CONGRESS CATALOG CARD NUMBER: 64-21664

PRINTED IN THE UNITED STATES OF AMERICA

PREFACE

This book is addressed to natural philosophers, whether science students or laymen, and attempts to convey something of the interest and fascination which attracts some scientists to crystallography and keeps them enthralled for the rest of their lives. Crystals fascinate for two reasons, one scientific and the other aesthetic. They hold within themselves the keys to an understanding of the solid state of matter and the way in which atoms and molecules are held together in rigid structures; they have played an important part in revealing the nature of light and of X-rays; and they have opened up a rich vein of three-dimensional chemistry which continues to advance knowledge on more than one frontier of science. At the same time the striking shapes of crystals, the regularities and symmetries of the arrangements of atoms within them, and the strange and beautiful effects on light and on X-rays are a never-failing delight to our aesthetic sensibilities. So for some of us they satisfy simultaneously both aspects of the contemplative side of our natures— the urge to understand the world we live in, and the desire to enjoy our experiences.

I have avoided formal or quantitative treatment of the topics covered, leaving that to the textbooks; instead, I have described phenomena and concepts in a general qualitative way, attempting to convey the essential facts and ideas to an imagined reader who is either an interested onlooker to the scientific scene or a scientist who is not yet a devotee of crystals. In the latter class I include beginner students of crystallography, who may find the book an agreeable preamble to their formal studies.

Most of the figures are original drawings, and here I want to acknowledge the great help given in their preparation by my son, Richard Charles Bunn. The following diagrams and plates are from other publications, and I wish to thank the following authors and publishers for permission to reproduce them: The Clarendon Press, Oxford, for Figs. 17, 26, 31, 36, 80, and 82 and Plates 9, 10, and 12, which first appeared in my textbook "Chemical Crystallography"; The Princeton University Press for Figs. 108

and 119, which first appeared in "The Chemistry of Penicillin"
(H. T. Clarke, editor); Professor J. M. Robertson and The
Chemical Society for Fig. 117; Dr. I. M. Dawson and The
Royal Society for Plate 5; Dr. G. F. Claringbull and The British
Museum (Natural History) for Plate 1; Dr. R. W. G. Wyckoff
for Plates 2 and 4; The Macmillan Company for Plate 7,
which first appeared in Sir Lawrence Bragg's "Atomic Structure
of Minerals"; Dr. Max Perutz and Imperial Chemical Industries
for Fig. 126 and Plates 11, 13, and 15, which appeared in
"Endeavour"; The McGraw-Hill Book Company for the photographs in Plate 6, taken from W. A. Bentley and W. J. Humphries'
"Snow Crystals"; and Dr. K. W. Horne for Plate 14.

                                                    C. W. BUNN
London, England

CONTENTS

GROWTH AND FORM

CHAPTER 1

The Crystal Kingdom

What is a crystal? The word, as used in everyday life, conjures up a variety of mental impressions: one thinks of the glistening grains in certain kinds of rocks; of "rock crystal" and, carved from it, sculptured figures in museums; of sugar, especially the kinds with large curiously shaped grains; of cut glass vases in shop windows; of diamonds and rubies and sapphires; of the simple "crystal and cat's whisker" type of radio receiver; or even of the fortune teller's "crystal" sphere. Not all these uses of the word fit in with its scientific meaning, which is what we are concerned with in this book; but the mental pictures roused by all of them include impressions of light—the scintillating reflections from rocks or sugar crystals, the radiant flashing beauty of diamonds, the reflections from the polished facets of cut glass, the more mysterious light effects within transparent objects, the cool silvery gleam of galena crystals used for radio rectifiers. The reflection of light and, often, transparency—these are the outstanding impressions we associate with the word "crystal." They are in fact the most striking qualities of the substances which were first given the name.

The word "crystal" comes from a Greek word meaning clear ice; but the word, and its equivalents in later languages, was applied not only to ice but also to transparent minerals, especially to the one now known as rock crystal or quartz. To get a clear idea of what a crystal is, we cannot do better than to look at a good specimen of this mineral. If you go for holidays to mountainous districts, you may find, in rock fissures, masses of very hard white material with perhaps (if you are fortunate) little transparent grains sticking out here and there, attracting attention by the scintillating reflections on their facets. Both the opaque and the transparent material are likely to be quartz, which is one of the commonest of minerals. If the transparent grains are large enough, you can see with the naked eye that their surfaces are flat to a high degree of precision, and it is this characteristic which is responsible for the scintillating reflections.

In certain localities, quite large crystals have been found, measuring as much as several inches across. The best specimens, which have found their way into museums, are truly beautiful and striking objects. A fine example is shown in Plate 1*; each crystal is a transparent prism of hexagonal cross section, finished off with a six-sided pyramid which brings the end of the crystal to a point. On some of the crystals, little facets may also be seen cutting off certain corners. In the Middle Ages it was thought that these crystals were a permanent form of ice, hardened by the intense cold of the mountains; hence the name "crystal," or clear ice. We know now that this is not so, for quartz and ice are quite different substances.

In earlier times, it was the transparency that excited most attention. Most rocks and mineral deposits are opaque, and the exceptional transparent ones were naturally regarded as curiosities; besides, the play of light on the surfaces and in the interior of crystals having such remarkable shapes is fascinating. And so the word "crystal," when it spread its mantle as words do over related objects and phenomena, became associated with almost anything transparent. The lens of the eye was called the crystalline lens, and the fortune teller's transparent sphere became known as the "crystal." There are still survivals of this association in everyday speech; we use the expression "crystal clear," and good quality glass of high transparency is called "crystal glass."

Later on, with the increase in knowledge of minerals and the growth of speculation on the structure of solid matter, interest shifted to the other remarkable feature of these transparent minerals—their precise geometrical shapes. It is not only transparent minerals which display flat surfaces arranged in a definite way; many opaque ones have equally definite shapes, with flat faces, sharp edges and corners, and some degree of symmetry, and with the accumulation of facts it became evident that this

---

* Plates 1-15 are grouped together following page 144.

sort of shape is a fairly widespread characteristic of mineral species. To be sure, specimens showing crystals large enough for their shapes to be appreciated by the naked eye are rarities; but sufficient of these rarities were accumulated by naturalists to suggest that such shapes were not to be regarded as isolated curiosities, but had a widespread and fundamental significance; moreover, the increased use of the microscope showed that many of the finer-grained mineral specimens, which to the naked eye are nondescript masses, actually contain small crystals.

The development of chemistry in the eighteenth and nineteenth centuries revealed a similar state of affairs among the many solid substances which were then made for the first time; many a chemist, stirring a cooling solution, was delighted by the spectacle of scintillating crystals whirling in the liquid; or came to his laboratory one morning to find that a liquid he had left the night before was now decorated with elegant needle-like crystals radiating in all directions. Even preparations which to the naked eye were nondescript powders were more often than not found to be entirely composed of minute crystals when examined with a hand lens or under the microscope. We can all repeat this experience for ourselves by looking at a few grains of sugar with a hand lens (the sort known as "yellow crystals" is best, but even "granulated" sugar will do, though the grains in it are smaller and not so easy to examine). The grains are by no means irregular in shape—they have flat faces at definite angles to each other, wedge-shaped ends, and sometimes extra facets cutting off the corners formed by the main faces (Fig. 1). The shape can be appreciated more easily in the large crystals sold as "coffee sugar." Table salt too is microcrystalline; under a hand lens it can be seen that the grains have a simpler and more symmetrical shape than sugar crystals, for they are simple cubes. Not all the grains are perfect cubes; many are damaged or broken during the processing of the material, and some may have been imperfectly formed; but sufficient cubes can be seen to justify our thinking of the cube as the "natural" form of salt crystals. The surfaces of the crystals of these familiar substances are far less perfect than those of good mineral specimens, but this is only because they have been damaged by rubbing against each other, and because atmospheric moisture tends to spoil their perfection. When the crystals are being formed in their solutions, the faces are often as perfect as those of quartz crystals.

The precise geometrical form—the mirrorlike perfection of the flat facets, and the overall shape which shows in different species varying degrees of symmetry—was to the early naturalists the most enigmatic, the most significant feature of crystals. Here was a demonstration that geometry is not just an abstraction conjured up by the imagination of mathematicians, for it appears spontaneously in the rocks. Here was a strong hint that in geometry is a clue to the inner secrets of the structure of solid matter. And so the word "crystal" was no longer applied to

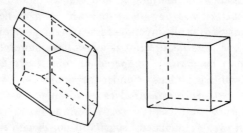

FIG 1.   Crystals of cane sugar *(left)* and common salt *(right)*.

transparent solids in general, but to solids which, whether transparent or opaque, showed in their natural state the flat faces and the symmetry which appeared to be characteristics closely related to their inner structure. This is the meaning the word acquired in eighteenth and nineteenth century science; cut glass, though it might be called "crystal" in the shops, was not so called by the scientist because whatever facets it possessed were imparted to it by human skill, they did not appear spontaneously. Indeed, glass was regarded as the antithesis of crystalline, because when it solidifies it does not spontaneously develop facets but takes on a round form like a congealed liquid. Scientists recognized two types of solid substance, the crystalline and the amorphous ("without form"), and glass was a typical amorphous solid.

The underlying basis of this distinction between crystalline and amorphous solids was the surmise that the spontaneous appearance of plane surfaces and a symmetrical shape was an indication of a regular and precise pattern of internal structure. The earliest recorded speculation of this sort seems to have been that published by Robert Hooke in London about 300 years ago in a book called "Micrographia." Hooke was one of the group of remarkable men who used to meet during the early years of the reign of Charles II to discuss natural phenomena, and formed themselves into the Royal Society of London under the King's patronage. Hooke, one of the most original and versatile of them all, thought that a crystal is a stack of spherical particles packed closely together in a regular way; and he illustrated his idea by stacking lead shot. Not long afterwards, in 1678, Christiaan Huygens (pronounced Hi-ghens) carried the idea further. Huygens was a Dutchman, and one of the foremost natural philosophers of his time, comparable in his achievements with Newton himself. He was remarkably versatile, being very practical as well as a notable theorist. He was responsible for important developments in methods of grinding and polishing lenses for telescopes and microscopes, he was the first to use a pendulum to regulate a clock, and his ideas on the structure of crystals and on the extraordinary effects of light in them are by far the most important in the early history of the subject. Some crystals, of which calcite or Iceland spar is an outstanding example, break (or "cleave") most readily along certain planes, giving pieces with precisely flat mirrorlike surfaces, and Huygens suggested that the cleavage planes are natural lines of division between flat sheets of particles. The cleavage planes, he thought, show the "grain" of the structure; but there is not just one grain direction in calcite, but three, and by breaking along these three planes a crystal of Iceland spar can be subdivided into little rhombohedra—shapes like cubes distorted by squeezing opposite corners together. The subdivision can apparently go on indefinitely, giving smaller and smaller rhombohedra, to the limits of vision, even when aided by the microscopes that were then available. Huygens thought that the ultimate particles might be little balls as in Fig. 2, but in calcite they would have to be flattened ("spheroidal") balls to account for the rhombohedral shape of the cleavage unit.

There the matter rested for over a century, until about 1800, when a French abbé named René Just Haüy put more precision into the idea of a regular stack of particles. Again it was Iceland spar that gave the clue. The story goes that Haüy was looking at a crystal of Iceland spar which had a pointed "dogtooth" shape, and happened to drop it on the floor, whereupon it broke into pieces along the cleavage planes. These cleavage planes are quite different from the natural faces of dogtooth crystals; the diagram in the center of Fig. 3 shows the natural faces at the

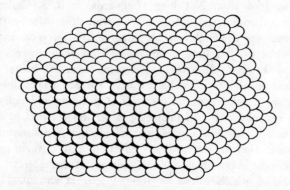

FIG. 2.   Huyghens' idea of the structure of calcite.

top and cleavage surfaces at the bottom, for this is the broken pointed end of a crystal. Contemplation of such pieces gave Haüy the idea that all the various natural faces could be accounted for as various simple ways of finishing off a stack of tiny rhombohedral particles having the angular characteristics of the cleavage rhombohedron; so he proceeded to calculate the angles between various planes in such a stack, and found that some of them correspond quite precisely to the natural faces. The diagram he gave in his "Traité de Mineralogie" is reproduced in Fig. 3; it shows how the natural faces could be related to the stack of rhombohedral units.

It seems, then, that crystals are composed of particles (much too small to be seen by the naked eye) stacked in regular array, closely packed in ranks upon ranks, and the various facets of any one crystal are various simple ways of finishing off the stack. If this were the origin of crystal shapes, then the differences between the shapes of crystals of different substances could be taken as indications of the differences between the shapes and the modes of packing of the tiny particles composing them. Moreover, substances like glass, which did not form crystals, appeared to lack this internal regularity. The distinction between crystalline and amorphous substances was thus thought to be a fundamental one; it was not just a matter of convenience in classifying solid substances.

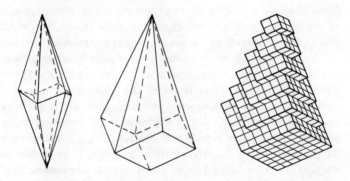

FIG. 3. *Left:* a "dog-tooth" crystal of calcite. *Center:* a piece with cleavage surfaces at the bottom. *Right:* Haüy's idea of the relation of the natural faces to the stack of tiny rhombohedral units.

In the present century we have learnt that this surmise was correct. New and powerful methods for studying the structure of substances—the use of X-rays and electrons—have shown that the stacking idea is quite literally correct. The types of arrangement of particles disclosed by these methods are sometimes more intricate than the early naturalists could have imagined, but the essential principle is the same. the plane surfaces do arise in the way they suggested, and recent photographs taken by the electron microscope actually show small particles stacked in regular array very much as in the early imaginative drawings. Two of them are shown in Plate 2. The particles are extremely small, far too small to be seen in any optical microscope (they are less than one millionth of an inch across). Only in a few crystals have the particles been revealed by direct photography, but in large numbers of others there is less direct but quite convincing evidence (as we shall see later) of this same sort of regular packing.

This, then, is the essential characteristic of crystals—they have a regular internal structure, with particles drawn up in ranks, packed in precise ways to form solid internal patterns, repeating over and over again in all directions in space. The plane surfaces are just simple ways of finishing off the stack, the relative slopes of the plane surfaces are settled by the fundamental measurements of the stacking scheme, and the symmetries shown by crystal shapes are indications of the symmetries of the stacking pattern.

This confirmation of the existence of regular arrangements of extremely tiny particles in crystals which show to the naked eye a precise geometrical shape is one of the great satisfying scientific achievements of this century. The common sense idea suggested by the shape is so completely vindicated: the details of solid patterns may branch out into fascinating intricacies (as we shall see later), but the essential principle is as simple as stacking boxes or billiard balls. Other natural phenomena may require difficult theories and unfamiliar ways of thinking, but the essentials of crystal structure are quite simple. The pattern units in a calcite crystal are, to be sure, not the simple oval balls of Huygens' picture or the little rhombohedral bricks of Haüy's (they are groups of atoms forming more intricate shapes); but these early naturalists did not claim that their models were correct in detail, they merely suggested quite reasonably that their pictures showed the essence of the matter; and they were right.

The new methods of investigation have naturally been tried on all sorts of substances, and it has been found that glass does not have the internal regularity of arrangement of particles found in crystals; so again the common sense expectation based on shape is confirmed. Glass in fact has the kind of internal structure found in liquids, in which the particles are disordered. The fundamental nature of the difference between crystalline and amorphous solids, which was suspected by earlier generations, is fully confirmed.

One result of present-day ability to investigate regularity of internal arrangement (or the lack of it) is that there has been a further shift in the use and meaning of the word "crystal." We have seen how in earlier times interest shifted from the transparency of certain minerals to their shape, and how this affected the use of the word; the significance of shape was that it suggested regularity of internal structure. Now that we are able to investigate internal structure directly, the emphasis has shifted on to this aspect, and with it the precise meaning of the word "crystal." Nowadays the word means anything having a precisely ordered internal structure, anything in which the particles are stacked in the way imagined by Hooke and Huygens. This change of emphasis is, after all, natural enough: external shape is a less fundamental character than internal structure. Crystals, when they are formed in rocks, may be so surrounded by others that they may not be able to develop the shape and the flat surfaces which appear spontaneously when formation is unhindered; besides, when a crystal is broken into fragments, each piece, though its shape may not resemble that of the original crystal at all, and may even be quite irregular, still has the precise regularity of internal structure which is the outstanding characteristic of the crystalline state. Such fragments would nowadays be called crystals, or at any rate would be referred to as crystalline.

As a matter of fact, even in earlier times, long before X-ray and electrons were discovered, scientists were perfectly well aware that many indefinitely shaped grains found in rocks or elsewhere were similar in internal structure to those whose shapes proclaimed them undoubted crystals. For external shape

was not the only characteristic which could be studied; crystals
have other remarkable properties in virtue of their internal
regularity—some strange and beautiful effects on light which
passes through them, for instance—and by observing or measuring
such effects it was possible to ascertain that, for example, the
rounded grains which are the chief constituent of the sands of
the seashore are nothing more nor less than little quartz crystals
which, by rubbing against each other, have lost whatever faces
they originally had. The story of the study of solid substances
is one of continual addition to the number which can be counted
as crystalline. To the original minority of minerals which by
their remarkable shapes first drew attention to themselves, the
microscope added the finer-grained minerals containing crystals
too small for their shapes to be appreciated by the naked eye,
the development of chemistry added most of the man-made
solid substances, while other studies filled in the picture by
adding the majority of indefinitely shaped particles found in
rocks or elsewhere. The newer methods utilizing X-rays and
electrons have continued this process of addition; it has been
found that crystalline regularity of arrangement of particles is
found in many solids too fine-grained for any optical microscope.
Even cotton and silk and some of the synthetic plastics are
partly crystalline in the sense that much of their substance
consists of tiny crystalline regions woven into their texture.

For this is the range of the crystal kingdom: most of the
substances of the mountains and the rocks, the soil which covers
the rocks, and the sands of the seashore; icicles and snowflakes;
all metals and alloys; diamonds, rubies, emeralds, and most other
precious stones; sugar and salt and soda, aspirin and sulfonamide
and penicillin, and the vast majority of solid chemical substances;
bones and teeth; and on its borders, hair and feathers, silk and
cotton, nylon and rayon, and even, remarkably enough, stretched
rubber. The crystal kingdom in fact comprises very nearly the
whole of the solid state of matter; not quite all, for a few important
solid substances such as glass and the glasslike synthetic plastics
and, above all, most living plant and animal tissues, do lie
beyond its borders; but it includes such a great majority of

solid substances that we may truly say that crystalline law and order are the rule in solid substances, disorder the exception; whereas in other states of matter—liquid and gas—disorder is the rule.

Law and order in crystals manifest themselves in the form of the regular patterns of arrangement of particles in space; these particles are the atoms and groups of atoms of which all matter is composed. We shall consider this in more detail later. For the moment it is sufficient to think in a general way of a group of atoms as a motif of pattern like the motifs of patterned wallpaper or textile fabrics, but solid instead of flat; and the repetition of motifs extends in all directions in space instead of on a flat surface—in three dimensions instead of two. Huygens' vision of a stack of particles is in this way elaborated by replacing each particle in imagination by a solid pattern motif. Bearing in mind that each different crystal species has a different pattern motif and that there are many different ways of arranging the motifs, we can envisage the crystal kingdom as a vast rich medley of space patterns, endless in variety of detail, but all conforming in their symmetries to the types permitted by the restriction of regular three-dimensional repetition. It is with these space patterns—the principles of their structure, how they grow from disordered matter, how the puzzle of their detailed structure is unraveled, and to what extent their useful properties depend upon their structure—that this book is concerned.

CHAPTER 2

Why Crystals Exist

I have said in the last chapter that most solid substances are crystalline, though a few, like glass, are not. What is the reason for this? Why is there a regular patterned arrangement of particles in most solids? Why are they not all like glass? To answer these questions, it will be necessary to say something about the atomic constitution of matter and about the way in which solid substances are formed.

A vast amount of evidence leads to the mental picture of all matter—whether solid, liquid, or gas—as composed of tiny particles which we call atoms. Some of the writers of the ancient world—Greeks and Romans—had an idea of this sort, though they did not know enough evidence to test it, and did not often do experiments to unearth more evidence; but in the development of chemical knowledge in the last 150 years, a great mass of evidence in favor of this mental picture has accumulated. We cannot see individual atoms, and even the electron microscope has not yet succeeded in photographing them, but the reasons for thinking that they exist are quite overwhelming.

The number of different types of atoms in the world is not very great—it is about one hundred—and every substance is made up of a selection of these. It used to be thought that every atom is permanent and indestructible, and, as a matter of fact, in ordinary circumstances most of them do apparently retain their identity through many changes of fortune; nevertheless, we now know that some of them (the "radioactive" atoms like radium) change spontaneously into different atoms, and others can be induced to do so by special treatment. However, we are not going to consider what is now called "atomic physics" or, more appropriately, "nuclear physics"—the change from one type of atom to another; we shall remain in the world of everyday life, the world of ordinary physics and chemistry, where an atom of oxygen remains an atom of oxygen, iron remains iron, and lead remains lead.

Atoms in interstellar space apparently lead solitary lives; but on earth, most of them form strong attachments to others, either of their own kind or of other kinds. These attachments are in some substances quite local; in water, for instance, which is made up of hydrogen and oxygen atoms (twice as many hydrogens as oxygens) each oxygen atom holds two hydrogen atoms, and this strongly bound group, known as a *molecule* of water, and referred to in chemical shorthand as H_2O, wanders about among millions of others. The sizes of atoms and the distances between them are now well known, and in Fig. 4 the

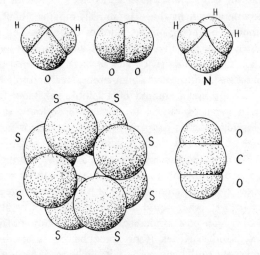

FIG. 4. Shapes of molecules of water (H_2O), oxygen (O_2), ammonia (NH_3), sulfur (S_8), and carbon dioxide (CO_2).

effective shapes of a few species of molecules, including water, are represented. The atoms are here drawn as spheres which, when joined together, are partly merged in each other; this simple picture leaves out a great deal of what is known about the structure of atoms, but it will be sufficient for most of the topics which are our concern in this book. Actually, each atom

is a cloud of negatively charged electrons with a positively
charged nucleus in the center, and the strong attachments
between atoms are due to partial mingling of their electron
clouds. The spherical surfaces in Fig. 4 are the boundaries of the
electron clouds. There is nothing fanciful or merely symbolic in
the molecular shapes depicted in this diagram; the molecules
of these substances really do behave as objects having these
shapes—and the dimensions have been measured by several
methods with results that are in excellent agreement. Chemists
and physicists, as well as crystallographers, often use models of
this sort, made accurately to scale, to help them in considering
the structure and behavior of molecules.

A glass of water must be imagined as a crowd of molecules
like the one shown in the diagram, all moving about, jostling
each other or bouncing off the sides of the glass. You may say,
how do we know that they are moving about in this way? Well,
first of all, the very fact that water flows suggests that the molecules must be able to move about pretty freely. Another indication is that if a small amount of a soluble substance like sugar
is put into water, eventually the sugar will be found in all parts
of the liquid, and this happens even if the water is not stirred.
Of course stirring will make it happen more quickly, but even
without stirring, the sugar will gradually diffuse throughout the
liquid; the particles must evidently move about spontaneously.
But a more realistic demonstration of the dynamic fine structure
of water (or any other liquid, for that matter) can be given with
the aid of a high-power microscope. If the water contains some
very tiny solid particles (they must be not more than one-
thousandth of a millimeter across), it can be seen that the particles
do not stay still, but move about continually: they quiver and
dance and wander about in an irregular way. Particles small
enough to show these movements well are rather difficult to
see unless a rather powerful side lighting is used; under these
conditions each particle shows up as a point of light, and the
sight of the irregular dancing of many points of light is a remarkable and beautiful spectacle. This sort of movement was first
noticed, or at any rate first described in print, in 1827 by a

botanist named Brown, and is therefore known as the "Brownian movement." The sight of it is one of the most surprising, and when one realizes its implications, one of the most thrilling experiences which the ordinary microscope is able to give. Its effect is not just a matter of the aesthetic impression of myriads of dancing points of light—there is more to it than that. Remember first that there is no question of the particles being alive: it happens with dead matter. When one realizes that this sort of thing is not simply a peculiarity of one substance, but is quite universal and happens to all small particles suspended in liquids and gases; and further, when it becomes evident that the movement never stops—it really is perpetual motion—one becomes conscious of being initiated into a great and fundamental mystery, the mystery of the strange behavior of matter on a scale so much smaller than the one we are used to that we are virtually looking into a new world. Particles on the scale of less than one-thousandth of a millimeter do not behave in the same way as larger particles: they begin to exhibit novel behavior; and if we are going to try to understand the behavior of the tiny objects we call atoms and molecules, which are even smaller— much smaller—than anything we can see in the microscope, we shall have to accustom ourselves to this novel behavior. The perpetual motion of small particles is in truth a phenomenon of the very greatest significance; it is the first great key to an under-standing of the ultra-Lilliputian world of atoms and molecules.

If particles of different sizes are watched, it can be seen that the smaller ones move more rapidly than the larger ones; it seems, then, that water molecules, which are a thousand times smaller than any particles which can be seen in the microscope, must quiver and dart about very rapidly indeed. And to complete the picture, the quivering or wandering movements of particles large enough to be visible must be due to the fact that each of them is being bombarded on all sides by many active water molecules, and the reason why it moves is that the impulses on all sides do not exactly balance: at one moment there is a net impulse in one direction, and at the next in a different direction. The larger the particle the more numerous are the water molecules surrounding it, and the more likely it is that the net impulses on opposite sides will be equal; so the larger the particle, the slighter the Brownian movement. Conversely, the smaller the particle, the fewer the water molecules bombarding it, the greater the chance of unbalanced impulses on opposite sides, and the more violent the Brownian movement. Molecules are so small that they must be dashing about in a great hurry—quivering or wandering at such a speed that even if we could see one of them we could not hope to follow its movements.

The necessity of accepting novel behavior, and even quite new ways of thought, is continually occurring in the progress of scientific knowledge; whenever we study the very large or the very small—anything far removed from the normal scale of our perceptions—we have to modify, or even completely change, our language of thought. In the still smaller world inside the atom, the necessary new language of quantum mechanics is so strange that we cannot honestly say that it seems to make sense (not *common* sense, anyhow), and our reaction is one of desperate acceptance of seeming incongruities. We shall not need to go as far as that in this book: much of the behavior of molecules towards each other can be understood without the desperate remedies of quantum mechanics; but the idea of the perpetual motion of the very small certainly has to be accepted, and, as we shall see, it does explain many things in a reasonable way.

But why am I writing as if strange new worlds can only be accepted with a certain reluctance? To some of us the very strangeness is itself a fascination: it has some of the charm of the exotic. I am convinced that one of the things that attracts people to scientific research is just this fascination of the exotic. No doubt there are various reasons why we study nature; the strangeness of what we find is not the only reason or the most important one. Apart from practical reasons, I suppose the most fundamental *personal* reason for wondering about these things and probing into them is that, after all, we are just trying to find out what sort of a world it is that we live in. Call it compelling curiosity, if you like, or say that we do it for the glory of God— that in studying the material world we are studying in all humility the outward form and face of God—but whatever you say, it is the most natural thing in the world to wonder how it is made and how it all works. *That*, I take it, is the most important reason; but the strangeness of what we sometimes find has a fascination which constitutes an important accessory reason. It holds our attention and helps to sustain us through difficulties and much labor. And that is not all: the strangeness we find when we explore the very small and the very large gives us a very salutary sense of humility—it shows us how limited are our natural perceptions. We are in danger of being imprisoned, so to speak, in our own scale of being, and the strangeness we find when we break through the barriers and explore a little way beyond them ought to warn us that there may be still stranger things further on, and that it is unwise to make general pronouncements about the whole universe or the nature of God.

Perhaps you think that I am exaggerating—that such reflections are scarcely justified by the contemplation of the Brownian movement and its lesson of the perpetual motion of the very small. Well, it is true that the world of quantum mechanics inside the atom and the vast world of the stars are even more exotic, and demand an even more thrilling leap of the imagination; nevertheless, it is scarcely possible to exaggerate the significance of molecular motion, not only because it leads to an understanding of a vast range of phenomena of the material world, but also because of its value as an exercise of the imagination. Indeed, the very moderateness of this particular imaginative leap into a new world—shall we call it a moderate leap into a moderately exotic world?—is something in its favor; those who find quantum mechanics or cosmology so remote as to leave them cold may perhaps find some warmth of meaning in the picture of bustling crowds of molecules whose behavior can, as we shall see, be understood in terms of common sense ideas.

So let us get back to our glass of water. Liquid water can, of course, be changed into steam when it is heated, or into ice when it is cooled. These changes do not alter the molecules themselves, but it is obvious that the relations between the molecules must be very different in the three different states of the substance. In the change into steam, an enormous expansion takes place, and the molecules in steam must therefore be, comparatively speaking, a long way apart; they are moving about just as in the liquid—or rather, they are moving much faster than in the liquid, and travel comparatively long distances before colliding with others or bouncing off the walls of the container. The change into ice is of quite a different type; there is not very much change of volume, but there is a drastic change of character: the flow, which in the liquid and the gas is due to molecular wandering, is stopped, and the molecules no longer move about freely, but settle down into a definite arrangement. However, we must not think of the molecules in ice as absolutely fixed and motionless—they are actually vibrating in various ways—but their mean positions are fixed; they quiver but do not wander. The essential difference between a solid and a liquid is that in a liquid the molecules move about freely, whereas in a solid they do not; and if the solid is a crystalline one, as ice is, there is the additional difference that in the crystal the molecules are regularly arranged.

Ice is quite typical in its behavior: most substances are crystalline at low temperatures, but on heating change first into liquids and then at higher temperatures into gases (see Fig. 5). These changes occur at very precisely defined temperatures, and they are reversible: if a gas is cooled, it first condenses to a liquid, and then at a lower temperature the liquid is transformed into a crystalline solid. There are, it is true, occasional exceptions to this scheme of things: some substances miss out the liquid stage and go straight from solid to gas or from gas to solid, and some on heating decompose (that is, change into other substances) before getting to the gas state or even before getting to the liquid state; but most substances behave as ice does, so that we may call this the normal behavior of a substance when its temperature is changed.

The foregoing discussion has been concerned with the drastic changes of state which occur at definite temperatures; but what happens to the molecules over the rest of the temperature range? If water is warmed from, say, 20°C to 60°C, it remains liquid, but something has happened to it, as you very soon find out if you put your finger in it. What has happened to it is indicated by the observation that as the temperature rises Brownian movements increase in rapidity; evidently the molecules are moving about faster. This is a quite general rule: rise of temperature of any substance, solid, liquid, or gas, is accompanied by an increase in the rate of movement of the molecules. The sudden increases of movement which take place when a crystal melts or

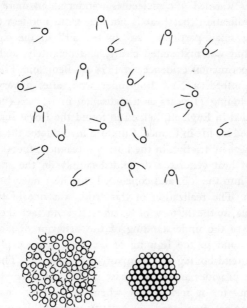

Fig. 5. Gas, liquid, and crystalline solid.

a liquid boils are the most spectacular examples, but actually the same sort of thing happens whenever a substance gets warmer. In fact, heat is nothing more nor less than molecular movement; it is not, as was once thought, a fluid which is added to a substance; the increase of motion is not just something *accompanying* warming—it is the very nature of heat. The amount of heat in a substance is simply the amount of energy of molecular motion. The feeling we have when we touch something hot is the feeling of increased molecular movement; and when anything is being warmed by touching something else which is hotter, what is happening is that the molecules in the hotter thing are passing on some of their energy to the molecules in the cooler thing (by bouncing against them) until both are at the same temperature. If a crystal is warmed, the vibrations of its molecules increase in violence; and if a liquid or a gas is warmed, the molecules wander about more rapidly.

This realization that heat is nothing more nor less than the motion of small particles was "in the air" in the eighteenth century, but was first stated clearly and definitely, and backed up by experimental evidence, in 1798 by Benjamin Thompson, Count Rumford, a New Englander who, after a very varied career including 11 years as a statesman in Bavaria (hence his title), settled in England, helped to found the Royal Institution, and finished his life in France. Rumford investigated the development of heat by friction in the boring of cannon, found that the amount of heat generated depended simply on the amount of work put into the job, and concluded that heat must be a form of motion. The realization of this truth was one of the most momentous in the history of science. It is in fact the second great key to the understanding of the behavior of atoms and molecules, and to the framing of common sense explanations of freezing and boiling and many other phenomena. The acceptance of it provides another exercise in learning a new language of thought—for it means that whenever heat or changes of temperature are mentioned, we have to translate these concepts based on sense feelings into mental pictures of moving or vibrating or rotating molecules.

The next question to consider is, "What is it that keeps molecules together at all?" If they are continually vibrating or wandering about, why don't they disperse and get further and further apart? As a matter of fact, that is just what does happen to a gas if it is not kept confined—it spreads out indefinitely; but for liquids and solids it is different: if you pick up a poker by one end, the other end certainly comes up too, so that it appears that the atoms of iron in the poker must adhere together pretty firmly; and a liquid, though it doesn't retain any definite shape, but adapts itself to the vessel it is contained in, does occupy a definite space—the molecules do hang together to the extent that if you half-fill a bottle with water, the water remains occupying the lower half of the bottle instead of expanding to occupy it all as a gas would; and if you pour water from one vessel to another of a different shape, it still occupies the same space; there is evidently something that makes the molecules of a liquid keep fairly close together and occupy a definite space, however much they may wander.

In dealing with this problem, scientists have used the idea of a force of attraction between molecules; just as the motions of the planets and the fall of a stone to the earth have been attributed to a "force of gravitation" which tends to bring large masses of matter together, so the fact that the molecules keep together at low temperatures is attributed to another kind of force of attraction between them. Such an idea is not the only way in which these phenomena could be made intelligible (as Einstein has shown for gravitation), but it is a homely concept which has played (and still does play) a great part in the development of scientific theories; we have to exert muscular force to prevent a stone from falling to the ground, and it is therefore natural to make theories which utilize the idea of force. In a similar way, a great deal of energy in the form of heat has to be supplied to water to separate the molecules and turn water into steam, and it is therefore natural to suppose that this energy has to be supplied to overcome forces of attraction. The forces of attraction between molecules, by the way, should not be confused with the force of gravitation; they are of quite a different order of magnitude, and appear to be associated with the electrical structure of matter. Although, no doubt, all fundamental phenomena are related in some way, it is best at present to keep inter-molecular forces and gravitational forces distinct and separate in our minds.

The two ideas we have been discussing—first, molecular movement depending on temperature, and, second, forces of attraction between molecules—lead to a mental picture of matter and its changes of state which seems fairly satisfying. At low temperatures, the molecules in a crystal are vibrating, but the forces between them prevent these movements from leading to migration and dispersal; when the temperature rises, the movements become more violent, so the molecules push each other a little further apart—in other words, the crystal expands a little. If the temperature continues to rise, eventually the energy of molecular movement becomes sufficiently great to enable the molecules to escape from their ordered positions and to move about freely—that is, the crystal melts; but the forces of attraction are still sufficiently strong to keep the molecules from flying far apart, except at the surface, where a few of them escape into the air above. (Even above cold water, the air becomes damp.) Further rise of temperature increases the rate of wandering of the molecules, and more of them escape from the surface, until a point is reached at which the molecular movements are so energetic that the forces of attraction are everywhere overcome, and the liquid boils.

The amounts of energy involved in these changes of state are very large; the heat energy required to warm a gram of water by one degree centigrade is one calorie, but to change a gram of ice at $0°C$ into water without any change of temperature at all is 80 calories, and to change a gram of water at $100°C$ into steam without any change of temperature is as much as 537 calories. Conversely, when steam is condensed to water, a great deal of heat energy is given up to the surroundings (which is the reason why it is possible to be very badly burned by steam), and when water freezes, the amount of heat given up to the surroundings is as much as when the same amount of water cools from $80°C$ (not far from the boiling point) to $0°C$.

In a crystal, therefore, there is very much less energy of molecular movement than in a liquid. Does this give a clue to the problem which was stated at the beginning of this chapter— the problem of the reason why most substances at low temperatures have the regular patterned structure which we call crystalline? Well, what we have to think about is, what is likely to happen to the molecules of a liquid when their movements are quieted by the removal of energy? If they no longer have sufficient energy to wander about, they will tend to settle in whatever positions their mutual attractions lead to. They are not able to do this when their energy of movement causes them to rush about; but give them the chance by cooling them down, and they will settle into comfortable positions. But what *are* the comfortable positions? For water, which has been used as an example in this discussion, one of the most important things that has to be taken into account is the electrical character of the molecules. In each molecule the hydrogen atoms are positively and the oxygen atoms negatively charged. Oppositely charged atoms attract each other, while similarly charged atoms repel each other, and so the most stable arrangement of molecules is that in which a hydrogen atom of one molecule is near an oxygen of the next and as far away from other hydrogens as possible. Now if every molecule takes up the same attitude towards its neighbors, this will result in the formation of a pattern because the same geometrical arrangement is repeated over and over again: in other words, a crystal is formed. This is, in essence, the reason why crystals are formed at low temperatures—it is because molecules settle into the most stable positions, and when all molecules take up the same mutual attitude, repetition in all directions leads to the regular patterned arrangement which is what we mean by the word "crystalline." The arrangement of molecules in ice is shown in Fig. 6; this diagram shows only one layer of molecules, and you will notice that on some of the molecules only one hydrogen atom is shown pointing to an oxygen atom of a neighboring molecule; the other is either above or below the plane of the paper, doing its job of attracting an oxygen atom in the next layer and so holding it in place.

Notice that the phrase "most stable" means "containing least energy"; for if water molecules are in the positions mentioned, with positive hydrogens near negative oxygens, it takes energy to put them into any other arrangement, just as it takes energy to separate magnets which have their opposite poles in contact, or to alter the arrangement in any way. If energy has to be supplied to alter the arrangement, then conversely the formation of this arrangement from any other must be accompanied by the giving up of energy. The arrangement that is most stable is thus the one containing the least energy. To be strictly correct, we shall have to say "least *free* energy," because not all the energy we can think of in molecules is available to take part in such changes of arrangement; but we need not go into such subtleties here.

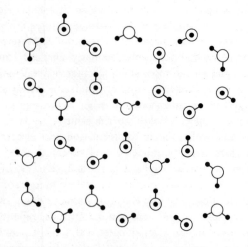

Fig. 6.   One view of the arrangement of molecules in an ice crystal.

There is one other consideration which it is important to notice; that is, that in the most stable arrangement formed by a large number of molecules, the mutual positions of neighboring molecules are not necessarily exactly the same as those which would be taken up by two molecules or a small number of molecules. Two molecules might form one particular arrangement, three a different arrangement in which neighboring molecules take up somewhat different positions; where large numbers of molecules are involved, repetition without waste of space imposes limitations, because, as we shall see later, only certain kinds of arrangement permit precise fitting in all directions, and the molecules have to do the best they can in the circumstances. There is nearly always one arrangement which is the most stable of any, and this is the one that is formed; but for some substances there are two or three arrangements which contain very nearly the same amount of free energy, and when this is so, the substance can exist in two or three different crystal forms.

Electrical forces seem to play a very important part in holding crystals together, and also, in certain crystals, in actually deciding which arrangement is formed. An even simpler arrangement than the one in ice is found in ordinary common salt crystals. Common salt consists of equal numbers of sodium atoms and chlorine atoms (NaCl). Now in a sodium atom one of its eleven electrons is rather loose, and is readily given up, while a chlorine atom is only too willing to add an electron to its own stock to make a total of 18 instead of 17. The reason is that particular numbers of electrons form especially stable arrangements; 10 and 18 are special numbers of this sort, so sodium loses one electron and is left with 10, and chlorine accepts it to form the stable 18. The result is that the sodium atoms are positively and the chlorine atoms negatively charged (and a charge of one electron per atom is a pretty strong charge.) When these electrically charged atoms, or *ions*, as they are called, have to find the most stable arrangement, they place themselves so that every positive sodium is surrounded by negative chlorines, and every negative chlorine is surrounded by positive sodiums; the arrangement is the particularly simple one shown in Fig. 7—a sort of chessboard pattern in three dimensions.

Electrical forces also play an important part in holding metal crystals together, though in a rather different way. Metal atoms all have rather loose electrons which they very readily give up; in a metal like copper, all the atoms are the same, and there is no question of some atoms becoming positive and others negative, because they all want to do the same thing and give up electrons. This is apparently exactly what they actually do—they all give up electrons to a common pool, and the resulting positively charged atoms are held together by the common pool of loose electrons; we can, if we like, regard the loose electrons as the glue that holds the positive atoms together. (Incidentally, it is the common pool of easily mobile electrons which is responsible for the good electrical and thermal conductivity of metals.)

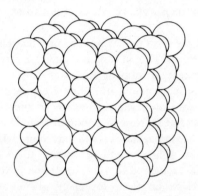

FIG. 7.   Structure of a crystal of sodium chloride (common salt). The smaller balls are positively charged sodium ions, the larger ones negatively charged chlorine ions.

The actual arrangements of atoms in many metal crystals are very simple—they are the arrangements we should get if we had a number of balls all of the same size and packed them together in the closest possible way (see Fig. 8); so in these crystals the actual arrangement can be regarded as just a matter of geometry (a consequence of the spherical shape of atoms), while the cohesion is due to electrical forces.

There is another class of substances, and a very important one it is, in which atoms are linked together in molecules as in water but there are no pronounced electrical polarities. For example, in oxygen the atoms are linked together in pairs to form molecules of the shape shown in Fig. 4. Since all the atoms are the same, there is no tendency for any atom to give electrons to another; there are therefore no oppositely charged molecules or oppositely charged atoms within any one molecule, and these nonmetallic atoms do not shed electrons to a common pool.

What, then, is the origin of the forces which make oxygen gas condense to a liquid at low temperatures and freeze to a crystalline solid at still lower temperatures? The forces are evidently comparatively weak, for a *very* low temperature (−218°C) is required to make crystalline oxygen, but forces there must be (if our conception that cohesion is due to attractive forces is

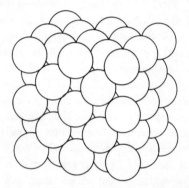

FIG. 8.   The arrangement of atoms in a crystal of copper.

acceptable). Another example of the same sort—and this time a substance which exists in the crystalline state at ordinary temperatures—is sulfur, which is found as yellow crystals of the shape shown in Fig. 9. It is known that the atoms are linked together in puckered eight-atom rings (see Fig. 4), and the crystal consists of these rings packed together neatly. But what holds neighboring rings together? Well, it appears that even

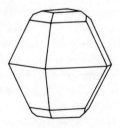

FIG. 9.   A crystal of sulfur.

here, electrical forces are responsible, but in a more subtle way
than in the other types of substances. We have seen that in the
world of the very small, continuous movement is a universal
feature. So far, we have considered only the movements of whole
molecules; but molecules do not move about as rigid things,
they vibrate inside: the dumbbell shaped oxygen molecules
elongate and contract very rapidly, moving in and out like
springs, while the V-shaped water molecules open and close
the angle of the V (as well as making other movements), and
the eight-atom sulfur rings are continually bending and distorting
and then righting themselves again. And this is not all: inside
the atoms there is the same restlessness. Each atom consists of an
electrically positive nucleus surrounded by a cloud of electrons;
the average position of the nucleus is at the center of the cloud
of electrons, but continual fluctuations make it momentarily
unbalanced electrically—it becomes rather positive on one side
and negative on the other. Since atoms in neighboring molecules
are all experiencing these fluctuations, there will be attractions
between them just as there are between water molecules, only
the attractions are less strong because they are due to random
fluctuations and not to the permanent polarities that exist in
water molecules. This is the present view about the forces which
hold together the molecules of oxygen and sulfur. Gasoline and
benzene and candle wax are other substances of this type.

A reason for the formation of patterned arrangements at low
temperature and a broad general idea of the forces which pull
the molecules into these patterned arrangements have now been
given; but if patterned crystalline arrangements are the most
stable, why isn't the formation of crystals universal? Why do
some substances like glass and barley sugar fail to form crystals?
Barley sugar, which is a glasslike, noncrystalline form of cane
sugar or sucrose, is a good example to think about. Sucrose, as
we know, can and does form crystals, but only if it is given the
right conditions; otherwise—for instance, if it is melted and then
allowed to cool quickly—it sets to the glasslike form. The reason
for the difficulty of forming crystals can be appreciated by
considering the molecular structure of the substance. Each

molecule consists of two linked rings of atoms (five carbons and one oxygen in one ring, four carbons and one oxygen in the other), with other atoms joined to the carbons; an important feature is the number of O-H groups sticking out from the rings (Fig. 10). Just as in the water molecule, the oxygen atom of each O-H group is negatively charged and the hydrogen atom is positively charged; and when molecules lose energy of movement by cooling, they tend to settle in such positions that the hydrogens of one molecule are near oxygens of the next. There is one arrangement which is better than any other (in

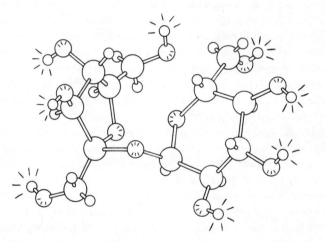

FIG. 10. A molecule of cane sugar (sucrose). The balls do not represent the actual sizes of the atoms; they merely mark the centers, and are drawn different in size to distinguish carbon (large) from oxygen (medium) and hydrogen (small).

the sense that it contains least free energy)—the one found in sucrose crystals; but molecules bristling with O-H groups may get linked with neighboring molecules in all sorts of ways, and most of these are not the arrangements required in the sucrose crystal. The chances are that the molecules get stuck in wrong arrangements. They can find their way to the right arrangement if given time at an appropriate temperature, especially if already formed sucrose crystals are put in as "seeds" on which other molecules can settle; but otherwise all sorts of wrong arrangements persist. As the temperature falls, molecular movement becomes more sluggish, and if it falls too quickly, the chance of getting into the right position has been lost, and the molecules settle down in the positions in which they happen to find themselves. The solid which is formed is a sort of congealed liquid, in which the molecules are irregularly placed, as in a liquid, but are fixed in position.

When a solid substance is found in a noncrystalline form, a reason such as this can usually be found to account for it: the substances which fail to crystallize are those whose molecules are liable to get stuck in a variety of arrangements. Metals, and simple substances like common salt, always succeed in crystallizing, if cooled to a sufficiently low temperature, even when cooled very rapidly: in order to form crystals, the independent spherical atoms or ions have only to get into the right positions —there is no question of orientation, for a ball is always the right way up; and anyway the arrangements are so simple that the right positions are easily found. These substances therefore have less difficulty in crystallizing than some of those whose molecules are awkward in shape or have a complex system of electrical polarities; in fact, metals and simple salts cannot be prevented from crystallizing, even under conditions which are least favorable for crystal formation. It is the large and complicated molecules that have difficulty in forming crystals, especially when they have a special arrangement of points of attraction.

CHAPTER 3

How Crystals Grow
I. The Birth of a Nucleus

The wonder and awe with which our ancestors contemplated the crystals they found in the rocks may perhaps have been accompanied sometimes by speculation as to how these remarkable objects got there. Whether or not people speculate on such questions depends partly on individual interest, but also on the intellectual climate of the time in which they live; no doubt in many countries and many ages, such phenomena have just been accepted without question—or if origins have been considered at all, the idea that the world was created suddenly in the form in which we know it caused the question to be shelved again, and the only significance attributed to crystals was symbolic or magical. But in times of free inquiry, admiration and delight are often succeeded by curiosity, and explanations of origins in terms of "natural causes" are sought.

We do not have to look far for a hint as to how some of the crystals in the rocks were formed. The freezing of water suggests that the crystals in rocks may have been formed in a similar way, by the freezing of material which was at one time molten. But this is not the only way in which crystals are formed; in fact, many of the finest crystals found in nature, including the quartz crystals which have already been mentioned (and illustrated in Plate 1), have grown from solutions: material dissolved in water has come out of the solution to form crystals. There is a third way also—it is possible for a crystal to be formed directly from a gas without going through the liquid state on the way; hoar frost consists of ice crystals which have grown from water vapor in the air, and a few mineral substances have been formed in a similar way, chiefly around volcanoes where sulfur and ammonium chloride crystals are formed from gases emitted during eruptions.

The formation of crystals from a molten substance has been discussed in the previous chapter, but only from the point of view of trying to understand why crystals exist at all. The regular, orderly arrangement in a crystal is formed at low temperatures, as we saw, because it is the most stable arrangement, the one containing the least free (that is, available) energy. But how is the orderly arrangement formed from the chaotic, hurrying crowds of molecules in the liquid? Do the molecules gradually get into some sort of order in a uniform way throughout the liquid, the orderliness increasing gradually until it attains crystalline perfection? Our experience of the freezing of water shows that this is not the way crystallization occurs. What happens is that tiny crystals form here and there, and these tiny crystals— "crystal nuclei," as they are called—then grow outward. In puddles of water, nuclei form on the surface, usually around the edge, and then grow across the surface until it is covered, and then downward until the whole of the puddle is solid ice. There is a striking contrast here to the formation of a glass. When a glass-forming liquid is cooled, it gradually becomes more viscous (thick, and sluggish in its movements, like syrup) until it is so extremely viscous that it may be said to be solid; this happens uniformly throughout the material.

There is another feature of crystal formation which it is important to notice. When a liquid is cooled, crystal nuclei are not necessarily formed as soon as the melting temperature is reached; there is some delay, and unless the cooling is done very slowly, the first crystals do not appear until the temperature gets very appreciably below the melting point—often several degrees. (The liquid is said to be supercooled.) The delay, and the fact that crystal nuclei are formed only here and there in the liquid, show that there is a certain amount of difficulty in forming the ordered crystalline arrangement. This is so, even in simple substances which never form glasses: even in substances which never completely fail to crystallize, there is some difficulty in starting off the process by the creation of nuclei.

When crystal nuclei *are* formed, they grow outward, steadily increasing in size; it is easier for molecules to add onto already formed crystals than it is to form nuclei in the first place. Usually, once the process of nucleus formation has started, the crystals grow outward until all the material is converted into a solid. There are other features of the process of crystallization of a puddle of water which are worth noticing because they are not peculiar to the freezing of water, but occur also in the freezing of other liquids. Notice first that when the ice crystals are growing outward, they do not have the symmetrical shapes that are such striking features of some of the crystals found in nature; they are often pointed growths, and although there may be plenty of evidence of straight lines, they are certainly not symmetrical solid figures with flat faces like the quartz crystals of Plate 1. But even if they were, they could not retain such shapes until crystallization was complete, for growth ceases only when the crystals meet, and in consequence the boundaries between neighboring crystals in the final solid are to some extent accidental. Many of the crystals in the rocks have been formed in this way, by the solidification of molten material; they consist of grains whose shapes are not necessarily characteristic of the crystal, and may indeed be rather irregular.

Thus the solidification of a melted substance does not usually result in production of well-shaped crystals. Most of the beautifully shaped crystals found among the rocks probably grew very slowly from solutions, not from melts. Many substances dissolve to some extent in water, and when a solution evaporates, the solid is deposited again. The volume of solid formed is only a fraction of the total volume of solution. If the number of crystal nuclei formed here and there in the solution is small, each is able to grow without coming into contact with others, or at any rate, if neighboring crystals do touch, it is perhaps only over a limited area, so that some part of each crystal grows unhindered. The solution may eventually dry off completely, leaving the crystals as we find them today in nature. The process may be imitated by making a solution of a soluble substance like alum or copper sulfate and leaving it to evaporate. It is advisable to leave the vessel in a place where it will be undisturbed, and to cover it, partly to keep out dust and partly to slow down evaporation; unless these precautions are observed, the number of crystals may be too large, leading to the formation of a mass of small crowded crystals. It is also advisable to take out the best crystals before the solution dries up completely, otherwise the last stages of evaporation are liable to produce a deposit of small crystals which may spoil the larger ones which grew in the earlier stages.

Another method of growing crystals is to make a warm solution containing as much dissolved substance as it will hold, and then to allow it to cool very slowly. At any particular temperature, water is capable of holding only a certain limited amount of dissolved substance—more will not dissolve; and usually, the lower the temperature, the less substance the water will hold in solution. When the temperature falls, therefore, the excess of dissolved substance comes out of solution, and provided that the solution is undisturbed and cooling takes place slowly, the number of crystals formed may be small enough to allow un-hindered growth of each of them. Many of the beautiful crystals of substances grown in the laboratory have been grown by one of these methods, or perhaps a combination of the two (that is, the first stages of growth take place by cooling and the later stages by slow evaporation). Whichever method is used, it is best for the solution to be undisturbed and for growth to take place slowly, the slower the better, not only because nucleus formation is reduced but also because crystals grown very slowly are likely to be more perfect than those grown rapidly.

Just as there is a delay in the formation of crystals when a melted substance is cooled, so also when a warm solution is cooled crystals do not form as soon as the temperature is reached at which the liquid can only just hold the amount dissolved in it. There is again some delay—the solution cools further, and at the lower temperature the amount of dissolved substance is really more than the liquid can hold: the solution is said to be super-saturated with dissolved substance, just as a melted substance cooled below its melting point is said to be supercooled. The delay indicates again that there is some difficulty in forming stable crystal nuclei. We can understand this difficulty in a general way. If a crystal nucleus is to be formed, what is necessary is that some of the molecules shall arrange themselves in the stable patterned manner required in the crystal. But in the restless world of molecules, it is not so easy to settle down to a quiet orderly existence. Even when a few molecules do happen to find themselves in about the right positions, they may still have so much energy of motion that they jostle each other out of these positions again; and even if they do not themselves ruin their own chances of survival as an organized unit, they may be so bombarded by molecules of the liquid around them that they are forcibly dispersed again (Fig. 11). The difficulty

FIG. 11.   A very small crystal nucleus may be dispersed by bombardment by energetic molecules.

of nucleus formation is a consequence of the continual occurrence of local fluctuations of energy, which arise in just the same way as on a billiard table, where energy of movement passes from one ball to another: a rapidly moving ball, in colliding with another, sometimes loses nearly all its own energy and practically stops, while the second ball moves off rapidly, having gained the energy lost by the first. If we imagine this sort of thing happening in a jostling crowd of millions of molecules, it is easy to see how a small group of molecules may at one moment be sufficiently calm to settle into an ordered pattern, but at the next be rudely disturbed by some more violent neighbors. So, even when a liquid is cooled below its melting point—which means that on the average the energy of molecular motion is really too small for continued existence of the substance as a liquid—and even though in several regions groups of molecules lose enough energy to enable them to settle down in crystalline formation, the chances are that very soon more energy arrives from a nearby concentration of fast-moving molecules and breaks up the ranks of what seemed to be a promising crystal nucleus. To be sure of survival, the promising crystal nucleus must attain a certain minimum size; once it becomes this size, it is not likely to be broken up again: its continued existence as a crystal is assured, and it goes on growing.

Actually, a liquid that is ready to crystallize does not necessarily have to rely on the entirely chance formation of ordered groups of molecules which manage to survive the hazards just mentioned. The laws of chance are often evaded, for the formation of stable nuclei may take place more readily on tiny solid particles which happen to be present than in the liquid itself—on dust particles, maybe, or on small crystals of some impurity which cannot be eliminated without a great deal of trouble. This is especially true if the arrangement of molecules in the dust particles is something like the arrangement in the crystal which wants to be formed—the molecules of the liquid, so to speak, find an anchor of roughly the right pattern, to which they can cling and so avoid being dispersed. It is likely that crystal nuclei are often formed in this way rather than by the unassisted chance aggregation of molecules in the liquid, for it has been found that sometimes scrupulous purification of a substance and protection from dust makes crystallization much more difficult.

The same is true for the formation of crystals from a solution; and it follows that if we want to grow large crystals by letting a solution cool or evaporate, it is advisable to get rid of any solid particles of impurity, and prevent dust particles in the air from getting into the solution, so that very few nuclei are formed. Good crystals of common substances like alum or copper sulfate can easily be grown by taking suitable precautions. First of all the substance is stirred with warm water until no more will dissolve, more heat being supplied to be sure of getting a solution which is saturated at a temperature a little above the ordinary room temperature. The solution is then filtered (through "filter paper") to remove any solid particles; the disturbance and the cooling may cause many nuclei to be formed, so these are dissolved again by rewarming. The solution is then put in a dish or jar covered with a lid, and left to cool until the next day. If too many crystals form, so that the final size is too small, the solution may have been too strong; remove some of the solid and dissolve the rest again by warming, filter off, rewarm the solution a little in case nuclei have been formed by the disturbance, cover it, and leave it again. If only a few crystals are formed this time but they are disappointingly small, the lid can be raised a little and propped up, so that slow evaporation can go on; if the solution is undisturbed, in a few days the crystals grow larger.

It is because nucleus formation depends on the slender chance of molecules arranging themselves and escaping forcible dispersal, or on the accidental presence of dust particles, that the behavior of cooling melts or solutions is often erratic. Different preparations of the same substance do not always start crystallizing at the same temperature. When a substance is heated, it always melts at the same temperature, but on cooling it does not always produce its first nuclei at the same temperature. Nucleus formation is a matter of probability, not certainty. The probability, of course, increases as the temperature gets further and further below the melting point, and most substances do eventually crystallize. But some of those that are capable of crystallizing when cooled slowly may fail to do so if cooled quickly, and instead set to a glassy form. This means that as the temperature falls below the melting point, the probability of nucleus formation increases up to a maximum and then decreases again; and if a substance can be cooled sufficiently rapidly through the temperature range of very probable nucleus formation, to a temperature at which nucleus formation is very unlikely, it becomes a glass, which may stay as a glass for years, though sometimes crystallization ("devitrification") may eventually occur through very slow rearrangement of the molecules.

Deposition on crystal nuclei, once they are formed, proceeds steadily: in a melted substance, until the whole of the liquid is converted into solid crystals; and in a solution, until all the excess material has come out of solution. This brings us to the subject of growth, which is a different matter from nucleus formation, and is dealt with in the next chapter.

CHAPTER 4

How Crystals Grow
II. Layer by Layer

It has been said that the beauty of a crystal lies in the planeness of its faces. Certainly the mirrorlike perfection of the surfaces of a well-grown crystal is one of its chief claims to our admiration. But it is not only our admiration which is aroused; crystal shapes are so curious that we naturally wonder first of all what is the structure of objects which form themselves into such striking shapes, and then how such structures are built up from the molecules of which they are composed. This feeling of curiosity as to how it all happens becomes particularly strong if one watches a crystal actually growing. Anyone who has a simple microscope (it need only have a moderate magnification) can experience this. If a strong warm solution of alum or sodium nitrate is made, and a drop is put on a warm microscope slide and covered with a glass slip, crystals will form as the solution cools, and grow rapidly—they seem to expand before our eyes. They are not, of course, expanding as a balloon expands— actually solid material supplied by the solution is being added on in such a way as to maintain the sharply defined shape—but they certainly look as if they are just swelling. Crystals grown under these conditions are often especially perfect jewel-like objects, beautifully transparent, with perfect edges and corners (see Plate 3a); and to see them visibly expanding while maintaining their jewel-like perfection is an impressive as well as a beautiful spectacle. One cannot help wondering how it all happens. We know that to build up the solid crystal, millions of molecules come out of the solution and arrange themselves in a precise, regular pattern. Do they sort themselves out into the correct arrangement in a wholesale manner, large numbers shuffling into the right positions by mutual accommodation, or do they add on to the surface one at a time, the way we should build up a model of such an arrangement by first making a single row, then adding a second, and so on until a whole sheet is laid down, to be followed by another on top of the first? Well, nobody has seen molecules or ions settling down on crystal faces, but the very fact that the crystals have flat faces does suggest that sheets are laid down one after another. If deposition occurred in the wholesale shuffling manner, it is not so likely that the surfaces would be flat; the correct internal arrangement could be attained whatever the bounding surface.

Confirmation of this idea comes from two different kinds of observations. Although no one has yet succeeded in seeing molecules or ions in the act of settling on a crystal face, there are two pieces of circumstantial evidence about the way in which they do it. In the electron microscope, crystals of certain proteins have been seen that have surface structures like that shown in Plate 4, taken by R. W. G. Wyckoff in Washington. The little dots are actual individual molecules (the measured sizes agree well with estimates given by other, more indirect, but nonetheless quite convincing, evidence), and it can be seen that the surface is made up of layers one molecule thick, one on top of another; furthermore, that the topmost layer is smaller than the next, and so on. The process of growth of these crystals from a solution in water cannot be watched in the electron microscope, because specimens have to be in a very high vacuum, and any water would just evaporate; the specimen shown in this photograph is a dried-off specimen of crystals whose growth has been arrested by the removal or drying up of the solution. Nevertheless, although crystal growth cannot be watched, this picture does suggest that the crystal was built up by the spreading of one layer after another, each spreading from about the middle of the crystal face.

The other piece of circumstantial evidence comes from observations, made under the ordinary optical microscope, of crystals actually growing. If a high magnification is used, it can be seen that on some crystals, layers do spread across the faces, one after another, and usually from a point roughly in the center of the face. Figure 12 shows the sort of layers seen on the faces of sodium chloride crystals. The layers which can be seen in this way are comparatively thick—many molecules thick—so that they do not really correspond to the molecular layers in the electron microscope picture; nevertheless, it can sometimes be seen that thick layers are built up by very rapid spreading of much thinner layers, suggesting that the same process takes place on a still smaller scale, perhaps right down to molecular dimensions. It looks as if the sequences seen in the ordinary optical microscope and the "stills" which are all we can get in the electron microscope are pictures of essentially the same process; together they suggest that crystals are built in just the way that we construct a model, by forming one layer after another. The only unexpected feature revealed by these observations is that the layers begin, more often than not, in the centers of crystal faces, not at edges or corners. Why the centers of faces are favored as the starting points for new layers is a question which has provoked much discussion in recent years; we shall return to it later.

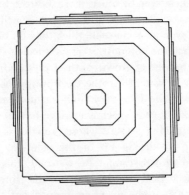

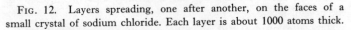

Fig. 12. Layers spreading, one after another, on the faces of a small crystal of sodium chloride. Each layer is about 1000 atoms thick.

Crystals, then, after being born in a somewhat haphazard manner—precious nuclei of law and order created out of the chaotic hurrying crowds of liquid molecules—grow in a method-ical way. One of the interesting questions about a newborn

nucleus is, "How quickly does it put on weight?" Now the
growth of a crystal nucleus is obviously a much less complex
affair than that of a living creature; surely, you might say, a
mechanical process of stacking molecules ought to be simple
enough. But the experiments that have been made and the
thought that has been given to the problem show that it is
actually far from simple; we can think of all sorts of things that
the rate of growth is likely to depend on, but very little is yet
known of the precise influence of the various factors. In the
first place, the rate at which molecules or ions can arrange themselves would be expected to depend on their size and shape,
and the strength of the forces acting between them; but it is not
easy to study the exact influence of these things, because there
are certain limitations, inherent in the very nature of crystal
formation, which complicate the whole situation so that it is
difficult to disentangle the various influences. We have seen that
when a crystal is formed, a great deal of heat energy is released
—and obviously, it is released at the crystal faces where deposition is taking place. Somehow this heat has to escape, for if it
stayed at the crystal faces it would accumulate until the temperature reached the melting point (or for a solution, the saturation
point), and no further growth could take place. What this heat
problem means, in the world of molecules, is that it is only
possible for some molecules to settle down in crystal formation
if these molecules have passed on some of their energy of motion
to neighboring molecules in the liquid, which are therefore
moving faster than before; until some of this excess energy is
passed on to other molecules further out in the liquid, those
near the crystal surface have no chance of settling down on the
surface. The rate at which the crystal can grow thus depends on
how fast the energy of motion is passed on by successive random
collisions—in other words, on how fast the heat "diffuses" away.
The slowness with which a puddle of water freezes right through
to the bottom is due to a similar limitation; ice covers the surface
fairly quickly because the cold air takes up the heat, but the
subsequent downward growth of the ice crystals is much slower
because the ground is warmer than the air, and therefore the

heat of crystallization has to diffuse through the solid ice to the
top, where it can be removed by the cold air.

In spite of the complicating effects of heat dissipation, we
should expect that, the colder the liquid, the more rapid the
growth of the crystals, because as the temperature is taken
further and further below the melting point, the liquid becomes
more and more unstable compared with the crystal, and there is,
so to speak, more and more incentive for molecules to join the
crystal—in other words, new layers would be formed more and
more rapidly. That this is indeed true was shown by the German
chemist Tammann, who is responsible for a good deal of our
knowledge of the formation of nuclei and the rate of growth of
crystals in melts. That the rate of growth, like the probability
of nucleus formation, reaches a maximum and then falls again,
has now been experimentally established; this is what we
should expect, because as the liquid becomes more viscous and
approaches the glassy form, the molecules become more and
more sluggish in their movements.

For crystals growing from solutions, one of the main factors
controlling the rate of growth must be the amount of material
available in the solution. Water is capable of holding about 35%
of its weight of common salt in solution; the supply of material
available for the growth of salt crystals is obviously not so
favorable as in the case of a melted substance freezing, where the
whole of the liquid can solidify; but the situation is far worse
for calcium sulfate, of which only one-fifth of one per cent can
be held in solution in water. We should expect calcium sulfate
crystals to grow from solution much more slowly than common
salt crystals, and this is indeed true. But many substances are
far less soluble in water than even calcium sulfate; only extremely
minute amounts of calcium carbonate or silica can dissolve in
water; the beautiful crystals of calcite and quartz (crystalline
forms of these substances) which are found in the rocks must
have grown exceedingly slowly, taking many years, even geological
ages, to have reached the sizes in which they are found.

There is also another way in which difficulties of supply of
material restrict the rate of growth of crystals from solutions.

When a crystal nucleus is formed and starts growing, some of the dissolved material comes out of the solution to deposit on the crystal; the solution immediately surrounding the crystal is therefore weaker than it was before. This obviously cannot go on indefinitely, for there would soon come a time when the solution would be undersaturated, and this would make the crystal dissolve again. What happens, of course, is that the weakening of the solution does not go as far as that: the concentration does not fall below saturation point. Growth would stop at this point, if it were not for the fact that material in the stronger solution further away diffuses toward the crystal faces, strengthening the solution there and thus providing more material for crystal growth. The rate of diffusion of dissolved substance toward the crystal is evidently an important factor limiting the rate of growth. Its effect is somewhat similar to that of the diffusion of heat away from the crystal. In fact, in the growth of crystals from solutions, both these processes take place simultaneously—heat is diffusing away from the crystal, and material for growth is diffusing toward it. Altogether these factors make up quite a complex process, especially as the shapes of crystals are often far from simple, and the diffusion processes around them therefore have to adapt themselves to strange geometrical situations. The limiting effects of both diffusion processes can be minimized by stirring the solution, so that the weaker warmer solution is continually washed away and replaced by stronger cooler solution. In this way, crystal growth can be accelerated; but the diffusion processes are always there; the effects are reduced but not banished completely.

The whole process of crystal growth from solution is so complex, involving the diffusion of heat and material as well as the key process of the arrangement and stacking of molecules as they join the crystal, that it has not yet proved possible to account in a quantitative way for the rates of growth of crystals in terms of what we know of molecular motions. I mean that nobody has yet been able to start off with some figures for the properties and motions of the molecules, work out the rate of growth of the crystal, and get the right answer. Indeed, the results of recent attempts to start from a consideration of molecular motions give the impression that it is difficult to understand why some crystals are able to grow at all. We have seen that the formation of a crystal nucleus in a melted substance or a solution is a very chancy business, because promising aggregations of molecules are liable to be broken up again by especially energetic molecules in the liquid: a nucleus must reach and pass a certain size to have a reasonable chance of survival, and this size depends on the degree of supercooling or supersaturation of the solution, among other things. It appears that even when the crystal has passed the critical size, the formation of layers on the crystal faces is subject to similar hazards. On a perfect surface of simple character, in which molecules are packed as closely as possible with no holes left, a new layer can only survive and continue to spread across the surface if it attains a certain size; when smaller than this size, it is liable to be dispersed again by energetic liquid molecules. The critical size for survival is smaller for strongly supersaturated solutions than for slightly supersaturated solutions, and therefore new layers are more likely to be formed when the solution is very strong. It has been calculated that on such a perfect surface, very large degrees of supersaturation are required to ensure the formation of new layers; at moderate degrees of supersaturation the chances of survival of a new layer are not worth talking about, and in fact a crystal with perfect surfaces cannot be expected to grow at all unless the solution around it is strongly supersaturated. Although these calculations, as they stand, do not necessarily apply to all crystals (it depends on the surface structure), they do indicate in a general way that the formation of new layers on virgin surfaces is a matter of some difficulty, especially in solutions which are only slightly supersaturated.

In actual fact crystals do grow even when the supersaturation is very small. It may seem that the conclusion reached in the last paragraph is a glaring failure of theory to account for undoubted facts. But the theoretical situation is not as bad as it seems; in the first place the calculations do not apply to all crystals, and, secondly, we have no right to assume that actual crystals have perfect surfaces—really perfect, with every molecule in the ideal position in relation to its neighbors. In fact, it is known that most crystals are riddled with imperfections of various kinds—cracks and dislocations (places where one part of the stack of molecules suffers a slight side-slip)— and it may be that it is the imperfections which make growth possible. The imperfections arise perhaps from strains caused by impurity molecules fitting badly into the structure; or perhaps by temperature changes: just as large-scale cracks in solid objects may be caused by heating or cooling one part more than another, so the minute (molecular-scale) cracks and other imperfections we are concerned with may be caused by temperature differences which are likely to occur during crystal growth as a consequence of the diffusion of the heat of crystallization. Certainly the existence of certain types of imperfection would facilitate growth. Suppose a miniature earthquake were to raise one part of a crystal face one molecule above the rest; the step would be the same as a layer edge, and molecules would add onto the edge. If such earthquakes were to occur continually, this would account for continuous growth.

There is one type of imperfection which is self-perpetuating; this is the type of imperfection known as a screw dislocation, in which the stack of molecules is distorted in the way illustrated in Fig. 13. Molecules readily add onto the edges of layers, and if this happens on the edge of the step formed by a screw dislocation, it can go on happening indefinitely; the layer is never completed, and the crystal, so to speak, grows "up a spiral staircase." Thus, continuous growth is assured without the necessity of waiting for the next heat-crack dislocation or for a brand new layer to start on a virgin surface. F. C. Frank of Bristol University suggested in 1949 that screw dislocations play a large part in keeping crystal growth going, at any rate for crystals bounded by close-packed surfaces and in solutions which are not very supersaturated; and very soon afterwards several people, looking at small crystals in the electron microscope (or even in the ordinary light microscope), came across some which show a spiral step formation on their faces, suggesting that

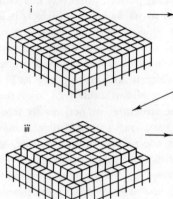
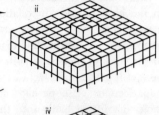
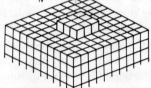

a.

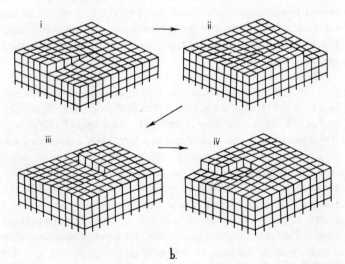

b.

FIG. 13.   Two ways in which crystals grow (on the molecular scale).
(a) Formation of new nuclei successively on the surface. (b) If there is a
screw dislocation, deposition on the layer edge can occur continuously,
in spiral fashion.

growth had occurred in this manner. A particularly perfect example is shown in Plate 5, an electron microscope photograph (taken by I.M. Dawson at Glasgow University) of a small crystal of a paraffin hydrocarbon (the type of substance of which paraffin wax is composed); the spiral formation is very clear, and it has been shown that the steps really are one molecule high. Unfortunately we cannot see the individual molecules; this is because they are very thin long things, end-on to the eye, too thin to show up even in the best electron microscope yet made; but the step height is the length of the molecules, and this is big enough to show up. The sketch in Fig. 14a shows the

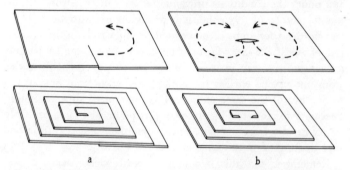

a   b

FIG. 14.   Thin crystals of paraffin hydrocarbons which have grown by continuous deposition on dislocated layer edges. (a) Spiral growth from a single dislocation. (b) Two opposite dislocations can give concentric layers.

surface structure from a different viewpoint. Still more interesting is the way in which the spirals from two opposite (left- and right-hand) screw dislocations near each other can join to form concentric layers (see Fig. 14b); this also was realized by F. C. Frank before it was observed experimentally. A photograph of a good example is shown in Plate 5b. One other point in favor of the screw dislocation theory of crystal growth is that it does account for the spreading of layers from the centers of crystal faces: for if a single dislocation, or a pair, is responsible for layer formation in the early stages, the point of origin will remain at about the center of the face as the crystal grows larger.

Not all crystals grow in the spiral dislocation manner. For instance, Wyckoff's protein crystal shown in Plate 4, which has a stepped layer structure in which one can actually see the individual molecules, does not appear to have grown in the spiral manner; there is no screw dislocation, or pair of dislocations, at the center of the layer system. Moreover, although various imperfections in the molecular stacking can be seen, there is no obvious connection between the imperfections and the layer structure. So for this crystal the question still remains: how did the new layers start? Maybe on this crystal brand new layers did start on a virgin surface; perhaps for this substance and under the conditions prevailing at the time when the crystal was formed (probably conditions of high supersaturation), there was no need for steps to be created by upheavels in the crystal. It looks as if the layer-forming process is kept going by various influences: the way in which layers are started probably varies from one crystal species to another, and even from one crystal to another of the same species. The amount of supersaturation necessary for the starting of new layers on perfect faces probably varies greatly from one substance to another, and also from one face to another on the same crystal.

Remember, too, that it is only on really close-packed crystal faces that there is a great difficulty in starting new layers; and such close-packed surfaces usually only occur on crystals of very simple structure. On many of the more complex crystals, especially those made of irregularly shaped molecules, none of the faces are really close-packed in the sense of having a well-filled surface without considerable hollows. If we were able to stop the growth at any stage and look at the surface, we should see part of a molecule sticking up here, and a hollow big enough to take an appreciable fraction of a molecule there (see Fig. 15); the addition of molecules to fill the hollows only results in fresh hillocks, and, in short, no surface at any stage of the deposition is ever really close-packed. There should be much less difficulty in starting new layers on such faces than on the close-packed surfaces (molecules are attracted into the hollows, and there would be sufficient forces to hold them there), and therefore we should expect surface nucleation to occur at much lower degrees of supersaturation.

But if it *is* possible for brand new layers to be formed on an undislocated crystal surface, why do they start at the center of the face? The cause must evidently be sought in events in the solution. Some recent studies have suggested that in an unstirred solution in which the concentration gradients around a crystal have had time to develop according to the laws of diffusion and are not disturbed by convection currents, more of the dissolved substance arrives by diffusion every second at the center of a crystal face than elsewhere (although paradoxically the solution is actually weaker there than elsewhere), and this may be the reason why layers start at face centers. If this is so,

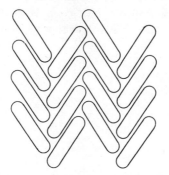

Fig. 15. The surfaces of a crystal of this type are not well packed, and have hollows in which fresh molecules can deposit; new hollows are created, so growth can continue. Growth is likely to be faster on the top and bottom faces than at the sides.

the movement of dissolved substance by diffusion appears to be more effective in starting layers than the sheer effect of supersaturation without diffusion flow. Such influences as this would be expected to be more important at high rates of crystallization (in strong solutions, strongly supersaturated, with steep concentration gradients maintaining rapid diffusion) than in very slow crystallization, which is perhaps more dependent on imperfections in the crystal.

It is only fair to add that probably not all crystals are built up by the layer-spreading process. Some crystals do not grow as solid polyhedra with flat faces, but as open-work skeletal structures by the rapid shooting out of arms in different directions; and the surfaces of these arms during growth are usually rounded, so they are probably not built up by the layer-spreading process at all. We must imagine molecules piling on in a more indiscriminate way, and getting into the right positions without forming flat layers. Skeletal growths are dealt with in more detail in a later chapter.

Sufficient has been said to show that crystal building, which is in principle so simple—a matter of stacking molecules or ions as a child stacks building blocks—turns out to be unexpectedly complex when we try to understand the precise way in which it happens and to find out what controls the speed of it. The transformation from chaos to order seems to be as difficult for molecules as for men.

CHAPTER 5

Some Stacking Patterns and Their Growth Habits

Hitherto I have treated a crystal as some sort of regular stack of particles, and tried to imagine, on the basis of the known facts, how such a stack forms itself and grows. But now I want to say something about the various types of stacking, how the type of stacking depends on the shapes and sizes of the building units, and what settles which faces the crystal will have.

We should expect that the simpler and more symmetrical the particles, the simpler and more symmetrical the crystal structure formed from them; and on the whole this is the tendency, though it is by no means always so, as we shall see. Crystals of many of the chemical elements (those containing only one kind of atom) are built by stacking individual atoms, and as atoms usually behave as spherical objects, the crystal structures are very simple. In fact, those of most of the metallic elements are, quite literally, the structures we should get if we packed a lot of ball bearings or table tennis balls as closely as possible. The packing of metal atoms in crystals is close, because apparently the atoms attract each other in a general sort of way without localized points of attraction, and pull each other into the most economically packed arrangement. In forming one layer, it is found that the most closely packed arrangement is one in which the balls are arranged in hexagonal fashion, each ball being surrounded by six others whose centers form a perfectly regular hexagon (Fig. 16a). The next layer can be formed by letting balls rest in the hollows between those of the first layer (Fig. 16b); this second layer is exactly like the first, hexagonal in pattern, but of course displaced in the sense that the balls do not lie directly above those of the first. In putting on the third layer, again the hollows are the natural places for balls to rest in, and the simplest thing to do is to let the balls of the third

51

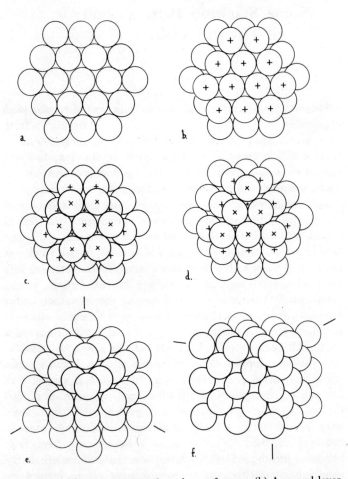

FIG. 16.   (a) Close packing of one layer of atoms. (b) A second layer,
resting in hollows of the first. (c) Three layers, forming a hexagonal
close-packed structure (third layer directly above the first). (d) There
is an alternative position for the topmost layer, giving a different structure.
(e) The same structure as (d), with more atoms added. (f) Another view
of (e), to bring out the cubic character of the structure.

layer rest in those second-layer hollows which lie directly above the balls of the first layer (Fig. 16c). This process can be continued indefinitely, and in this way a structure is built up which corresponds to the structures of crystals of some of the metallic elements—zinc, magnesium, cadmium, and others. This arrangement is known as "hexagonal close packing"; the word "hexagonal" refers not only to the hexagonal pattern of each layer, but to the fact that the complete arrangement has hexagonal symmetry.

There is another arrangement, equally close-packed, and constructed on the same principles as the first, which, however, does not possess hexagonal symmetry. If two layers are put down in exactly the same way as before, there is for the third layer an alternative position; instead of putting the balls so that they lie exactly above those of the first layer, they can be put in another set of hollows as in Fig. 16d. Although each individual layer in this structure is hexagonal in character, the complete structure does not have hexagonal symmetry, but only (for this aspect) trigonal symmetry. This arrangement is also a very common one; crystals of most of the metallic elements, if they do not have the first-mentioned hexagonal arrangement, have this second arrangement which, however, is not called trigonal close packing because on closer examination it is found to have many more symmetries and is in fact cubic in character. It is not easy to see this unless one has actual models to play with, but in Figs. 16e and 16f the arrangement is depicted in such a way as to bring out the cubic character. It is not an entirely simple cubic pattern, for if a cubic unit is picked out—a group of atoms such that there is one atom at each corner of a cube— it can be seen that there are also atoms at the centers of the cube faces; for this reason the arrangement is known as "face-centered cubic," or "cubic close packing." This is the structure of copper, already illustrated in Fig. 7, and of silver, gold, aluminum, and various other metals.

It is evident that, in trying to grasp the character of packing patterns such as the two arrangements just described, there are two things to do—to look for the type of symmetry, and to pick

out an appropriate unit of structure. For the present we shall
concentrate on the unit of structure. Any repeating pattern can
be divided into units of pattern, all exactly the same as each
other, and all touching each other without leaving any holes;
for patterns on a flat surface, such as wallpapers or textile
fabrics, the unit is an area bounded by two pairs of parallel
straight lines, as in Fig. 17. There is a certain amount of freedom

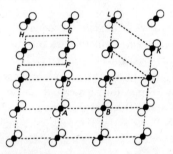

FIG. 17. A plane pattern. Lower part divided into identical unit
cells such as *ABCD*. Alternative cells *EFGH* and *IJKL* are also outlined.

of choice in selecting the unit; for instance, in this pattern, the
area *ABCD* is an obvious choice for the unit; but we might
have started at a different point *E* and chosen the area *EFGH*,
which has exactly the same shape as *ABCD*, but is set differently
in the pattern. Equally well, the area *IJKL* could be chosen;
it contains one unit of pattern, and has exactly the same area
as *ABCD* or *EFGH*, but has a different shape; and many other
still more elongated areas, each containing one unit of pattern,
could be drawn. In practice it is usually most convenient to
accept as the unit of pattern the area with the shortest sides
and with angles nearest to right angles. For the more highly
symmetrical patterns it may be possible to choose units with
exactly equal sides or with precise right angles—units which
would be not only more convenient but more appropriate to the
nature of the pattern than other shapes having the same area.
And notice also that the most appropriate unit need not necessarily

contain only one element of pattern—it may contain two or more; for example, in the pattern of Fig. 18 the unit *ABCD* containing two elements of pattern is more appropriate than the smaller unit *EFGH* containing one element, because the first brings out the rectangular character while the second does not.

Exactly the same principles apply to patterns in space, which can always be divided into boxlike units of pattern known as "unit cells." In the face-centered cubic arrangement mentioned

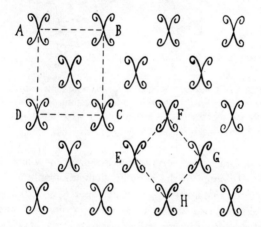

Fig. 18.   The unit area *ABCD* comprising two pattern motifs is more appropriate than the one-motif unit *EFGH* because it brings out the rectangular character of the pattern.

a little way back, the building unit is a single spherical atom, but the cubic unit cell contains more than one atom. Actually the number is four; this is not immediately obvious, but can be seen in the following way. The unit cell, Fig. 19a, is a box with an atom at each corner; there are eight corners to a cube, but part of each corner atom is in each of the eight cubes which meet there, so that for corner atoms we have one per cube. Part of each atom at a face center is in each of the two cubes which meet at that face, and as there are six faces to a cube and half an atom to each face, there are for face atoms three per cube; so the total is four per cube. It would be possible to choose a unit cell having only one atom per cell as in Fig. 19b, but such a unit would not have a cubic shape; the four-atom cubic unit is obviously more appropriate, because it brings out the cubic character.

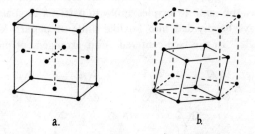

a.   b.

Fig. 19. (a) Unit cell of face-centered cubic structure of copper and some other metals. Only the centers of atoms are marked, so that it is possible to see through the structure. (b) A one-atom unit cell would not be appropriate for this structure.

There is one other very simple arrangement which is found in crystals of some of the metallic elements (sodium, iron, and tungsten, for instance); this arrangement (Fig. 20) has a unit cell containing two atoms, one at the corner and one at the center of a cube, and is accordingly known as the "body-centered cubic" structure. It is not what is called a "close-packed"

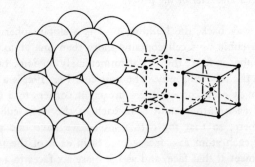

Fig. 20. Body-centered cubic structure. Crystals of sodium, iron, and tungsten have this structure.

structure, because spherical balls arranged in this way take up appreciably more space than in the two close-packed structures; the existence of this more open arrangement may be interpreted as meaning either that the atoms in these crystals are not effectively spherical, or else that they are held together not by vague general attractions but by directional forces.

Nonmetallic elements usually form more complex and sometimes less symmetrical crystals than the metals. The reason for this is that these atoms form strong localized attachments to others; for instance, in oxygen, nitrogen, and iodine, the atoms are tightly joined in pairs, and the shape of a two-atom molecule such as O_2, N_2, or I_2 is like that of a pair of partly merged spheres. (See Fig. 4.) (The electron clouds of the two atoms actually intermingle to some extent.) The packing together of molecules of this shape naturally leads to the formation of more complex crystal structures than in those of the metals. One such structure, that of iodine, is illustrated in Fig. 21. (Iodine

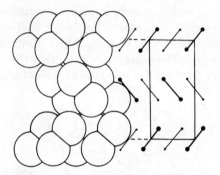

Fig. 21.   Arrangement of molecules found in crystals of iodine and chlorine.

is a substance which is usually in the form of metallic-looking flakes which, on warming, soon show how very unmetallic they really are by changing into violet vapor.) The molecules in the crystal are not all oriented in the same way: half of them are, so to speak, tilted one way and half the other way. What settles the exact angle of tilt is not known in detail; it is probably partly a matter of shape—the molecules pack better this way than they would if they were all parallel—and partly a matter of localized attractions which favor this sort of mutual orientation.

The unit cell is certainly not a cube in this crystal—far from it. It is a rectangular box with quite unequal sides—what the crystallographer calls an orthorhombic cell. Chlorine molecules also arrange themselves in this way. Chlorine is the gas used in water purification and for many other purposes, and it is the gas you can smell in the solution of sodium hypochlorite often used as a disinfectant. Only when cooled to a very low temperature does it solidify, but when it does the molecules arrange themselves in the same way as those of iodine.

In iodine each atom is tightly joined to only one other atom. But other atoms can join to two or more others, and this naturally leads to the formation of more complex and more interesting types of molecules. A sulfur atom joins to two others, and the continuation of this leads to the formation of chains and rings of sulfur atoms; such versatility in molecule formation naturally leads to varied crystal structures, but here I shall only mention one, the most stable crystal form, which contains puckered eight-atom rings. The arrangement, or rather part of it, is shown in Fig. 22; again the molecules are not all oriented in the

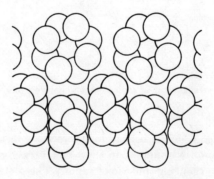

FIG. 22. Arrangement of molecules in a crystal of sulfur. (Only a part of the complete arrangement is shown.)

same way, and as a matter of fact the unit cell comprises no less than eight of them; and again the unit cell is of the orthorhombic type, rectangular but with unequal edges. Only enough of the arrangement is shown to bring out the way in which neighboring molecules fit in with one another; notice how, to ensure efficient packing, the knobs of one molecule fit into the hollows of its neighbors.

Atoms capable of linking to three or four others can form networks—either sheetlike, or else stretching out in all directions in space. The star element for this accomplishment is carbon which, with its capacity for joining strongly to four others, can form three-dimensional networks of unlimited size. But there are rules—strict rules—about the formation of the network: the four links joining any one carbon atom to its four neighbors must be equally distributed in space—that is, the angles between the four must all be equal; this configuration of links is known as the "tetrahedral" configuration, because the links can be thought of as directed from the center of a regular tetrahedron towards its four corners, as in Fig. 23a. The repetition of this

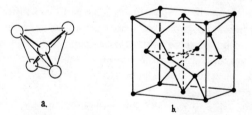

a.   b.

FIG. 23.   (a) Tetrahedral arrangement of the four links (or "bonds") of a carbon atom. (The sizes of the spheres do not represent the real sizes of the atoms.) (b) The structure of diamond. (The atoms are all interlinked, each to four others, but the links of the atoms on the corners and edges of the unit cube are not all shown.)

tetrahedral arrangement of links leads to the structure shown in Fig. 23b, which is nothing more nor less than the arrangement of atoms in diamond. The unit cell is again a cube, with four atoms to each unit; but the whole arrangement is quite different from the face-centered cubic structure which also has four atoms to the unit cube, because in diamond each atom has only four nearest neighbors, whereas in a face-centered cubic metal like copper each atom has twelve nearest neighbors.

The extraordinary qualities of diamond, the undoubted queen of the crystal kingdom, will be discussed in a later chapter, but there is one aspect which can appropriately be dealt with here. A glance at the picture of the structure in Fig. 23b may give the impression of a rather open structure; this is partly because it is drawn in a skeletal fashion instead of as a stack of spheres; but even if it had been drawn as a stack of spheres just touching each other it would still look rather open, because each atom is surrounded by only four others instead of the twelve in the close-packed structures or the eight in the body-centered cubic structure. The impression of openness is, however, entirely misleading; carbon atoms in diamond are not merely stacked, they are actually joined together by very powerful forces; they are joined by what the chemist calls "primary bonds," which pull atoms so close together that their electron clouds partly intermingle, so that the distance between carbon atom centers in diamond is much less than the known diameter of a carbon atom. For this reason it would be misleading to represent the diamond structure as an open stack of small spheres just touching; on the contrary, it is a highly compressed structure, in which the atoms are squashed by the powerful forces between them.

Another striking thought about diamond is that a crystal of this substance is quite literally one colossal molecule. We often talk about molecules as extraordinarily small things, far too small to be seen with the naked eye, and most of them too small even to be seen in the best electron microscope; and this is true for most molecules. But for diamond it is not true—each crystal is a molecule; there may be flaws in it, where the tetra-hedral linking scheme is broken locally, but the crystal is, in intention, one colossal molecule.

Diamond is not the only sort of crystal formed by carbon atoms. Graphite, the black substance in so-called soft "lead pencils," has nothing to do with lead, and is simply another crystal form of carbon. The difference between graphite and diamond is that in graphite each carbon atom is joined to only three others, not four, and the threefold linking scheme is subject to a different space rule from that which holds in diamond. The three links must all lie in a plane, and repetition of this results in the formation of a flat honeycomblike network; a graphite crystal is simply a pile of these flat honeycombs, as in Fig. 24.

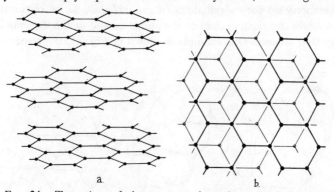

a.   b.

FIG. 24.   Two views of the structure of graphite. (a) Side view of the pile of honeycomblike molecules. (b) Plan to show the exact manner of packing of one molecule on the next.

Each flat honeycomb is a large molecule, extending all the way through each crystal, but only one atom thick. The profound importance of atomic arrangement in settling the properties of matter is nowhere more strikingly demonstrated than in the contrast between diamond and graphite: the one extremely hard and transparent, the other soft and black, but both composed only of carbon atoms. Geometry is no mere abstract study, fit only for dreamers with their heads in the clouds: it is the very basis of the properties of matter which rule our lives.

A chemical "compound" is a substance containing two or more types of atoms linked together; the structures of the crystals of compounds depend, just as do those of the elements, on the way in which the atoms are linked together. If the atoms are all joined by powerful primary bonds in strictly defined directions as in diamond, the crystal structure is simply the extended expression of this linking scheme. In carborundum (silicon carbide, SiC), for example, the structure is built on the same general principles as in diamond, except for the alternation of the two types of atoms, carbon and silicon. But if there are molecules of limited size, the strict directional linking scheme only holds within each molecule, and the crystal structure is a stack of molecules (as in iodine and sulfur) depending for its geometry on the overall shape of the molecule which obviously involves the relative sizes of the atoms as well as the directional linking scheme. One example is shown in Fig. 25, the structure

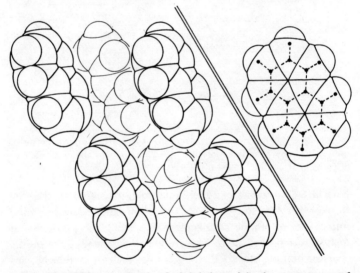

FIG. 25.   *Right:* a molecule of naphthalene; *left:* the arrangement of molecules in the crystal.

of naphthalene, a substance used as a moth repellant and garden insecticide. A molecule of naphthalene consists of two hexagonal rings of carbon atoms joined together, with hydrogen atoms attached to the outer carbon atoms to form a border of smaller atoms, the whole molecule being a flattish object having the general shape depicted; the crystal structure is an economical packing of these shapes. As in iodine and sulfur, the molecules are not all parallel to each other—half are tilted one way and half the other; but notice that the arrangement is less symmetrical than any of those mentioned before—it has a "skew" character, presumably because molecules of this shape pack better and satisfy each other's local attractions better in this skew fashion than they could in a rectangular or highly symmetrical fashion.

The clearest and most striking effects of relative atomic sizes are shown by the structures of some of the simple chemical salts, in which the building units are single electrically charged atoms ("ions"). The word "salt," in chemistry, means a substance composed of positively charged metal atoms, called "ions," and negatively charged ions of nonmetallic character. In the simplest type of salt, of which common salt or sodium chloride (NaCl) is the most familiar example, both the ions are single atoms, electrically charged, with equal and opposite charges, and in crystals of these salts, equal numbers of the two different ions are held together by the strong electrical attractions between the positive metal ions and the negative nonmetallic ones. There are no specific links and apparently no directional forces between the ions, only general attractions, and the sort of arrangement that is built up depends on two principles: (1) the local satisfaction of electric fields, which causes positive ions to be surrounded by negative ones (and negative ones to be surrounded by positive ones), and (2) the relative sizes of the two kinds of ions. If they are much the same size, any one ion is surrounded by eight of the opposite kind, and the arrangement has a cubic unit cell with one kind of ion at the corners and the other at the centers of the cells, as in Fig. 26a. There is no example among common substances, but cesium bromide (CsBr) has this structure: caesium is a bigger and heavier (and rather rare) member of the sodium family of atoms, while bromide is a bigger and heavier member of the chlorine family of atoms. If one has roughly half the diameter of the other (the actual ratio can vary widely from about 0.4 to 0.8), only six of the larger ones can get round one of the smaller ones, and the arrangement formed is the sort of three-dimensional chessboard pattern

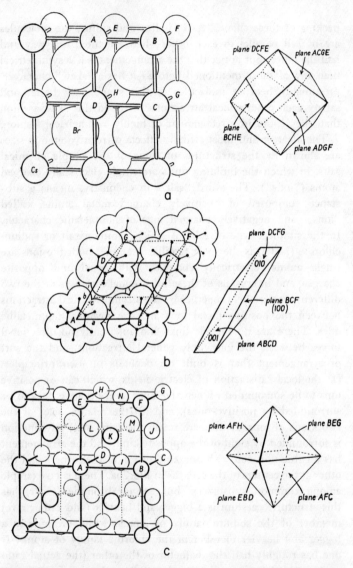

FIG. 26. (a) Cesium bromide, CsBr. *Left:* structure; *right:* shape of crystal. (b) Hexamethylbenzene, $C_6(CH_3)_6$. *Left:* structure; *right:* shape of crystal. (c) Copper. *Left:* structure; *right:* shape of crystal.

shown earlier in Fig. 7; the actual one illustrated is sodium chloride, common salt itself, in which the sodium ion is just over half the size of the chlorine ion. Notice that sodium ions by themselves form a face-centered cubic pattern, but so also do the chlorines by themselves, the two patterns being inter-penetrating.

The structures mentioned so far have been fairly simple, and most of them highly symmetrical. Increasing complexity or declining symmetry of the building units leads to crystal structures with unit cells which are either symmetrical but large and complex in content (with a number of differently oriented molecules arranged in symmetrical fashion), or else not so large but of low symmetry. We shall not consider such structures in any detail here; some will be encountered in the course of later chapters, but for the moment we are concerned with the general principles of stacking, and the only examples mentioned will be to illustrate these principles. It will be clear, from the examples already considered, that the shape and characteristics of molecules do not necessarily appear in an obvious way in the structure of the crystal; naphthalene molecules, which are, after all, flat, fairly symmetrical objects (Fig. 25), form crystals with a skew character (the crystallographer calls it "monoclinic"), presumably because they pack better and satisfy each other's local attractions better in this arrangement than they could in any arrangement having the same sort of symmetry as the molecules themselves. A still more glaring example of this sort of thing is the substance hexamethylbenzene; individual molecules have full hexagonal symmetry—there is an inner ring of six carbon atoms, to each of which is attached another carbon atom carrying three hydrogen atoms. But do they pack in hexagonal fashion? Not a bit of it; the crystal structure (Fig. 26b) is "skew" in all directions— what the crystallographer calls triclinic, the least symmetrical of all types. Again this is presumably because local attractions and the requirements of good packing are not satisfied by an arrange-ment of hexagonal character; so the symmetries of the molecule are ignored in the building of the crystalline arrangement. In compensation, so to speak, for the low symmetry, the unit cell

comprises only one molecule; it is as simple as it can be, in
that way. This is very often so; what we lose on the swings we
gain on the roundabouts; very frequently indeed, we find that
a crystal composed of molecules is either complex but with
high symmetry, or else simple but with low symmetry.

Having looked at a few stacking schemes, consider the crystal
faces and their relation to the stack. I have said several times
that crystal faces are simple ways of finishing off the stack;
but now look into this more closely and think what it means.
Crystals are built up layer by layer, and it is natural that the
surfaces chosen for the layer-forming process would be the
most layerlike in character—in other words, planes having the
greatest density of particles *in* each layer and the greatest distance
between one layer and the next (see Fig. 27). We can connect

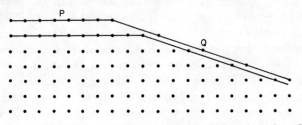

FIG. 27.   Plane *P* is more likely to be a natural face than plane *Q*.

this with what we know of the geometry of growth. If a cubic
crystal is reduced to a rounded shape by grinding or by dissolving
off the outside, and put into a supersaturated solution, first of
all small faces appear on the corners and edges, but these grow
outward faster than the cube faces, and eliminate themselves in
the way illustrated in Fig. 28, which is a section through the
middle of the crystal. This experiment demonstrates that the
bounding faces of a crystal are those with the slowest rate of
thickening, which means (if growth occurs by the starting of
brand new layers, not by the dislocation mechanism) the greatest
intervals of time between the starting of one layer and of the
next. It is natural to expect that the starting of a new layer would
be more difficult on a well-packed surface than on a more open

surface, because in a poorly packed surface there are considerable hollows into which new molecules can fit (attractive forces pull them in) and when they are installed they stick up and form new hollows; whereas on a well-packed surface there are only slight hollows. So new layers would be expected to be formed at longer intervals of time on well-packed surfaces, which therefore would have lower rates of thickening than others and therefore would become the bounding surfaces.

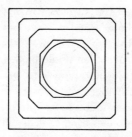

FIG. 28. Successive stages of growth of a rounded crystal of sodium chlorate, when put into supersaturated solution. At first, small corner faces as well as cube faces are formed; but as the crystal grows, the corner faces, which grow faster, eliminate themselves.

This expectation is very often realized, in those simple crystals to which these simple ideas apply. For instance, crystals of many of the metals that have the face-centered cubic structure grow as regular octahedra (Fig. 26c). The relation of the surfaces of the octahedron to the atomic pattern is made clear in the diagram—each face, so to speak, cuts off a corner of the cubic unit cell in a symmetrical manner. These surfaces are the most close-packed ones it is possible to find in this structure. Similarly, some of the simple salts which have the structure of caesium bromide grow in the form of a rhombic dodecahedron, the twelve-faced shape shown in Fig. 26a; the faces are again the planes which are most densely packed with atoms. But with salts we shall have to be careful: they are stacks of positive and negative ions, and the surface forces depend on the distribution of electric charges in the surface as well as on the closeness of surface packing. A plane consisting entirely of positive ions, or entirely of negative ions, would attract ions of the opposite sort so strongly that new layers would be expected to be formed very rapidly, and for this reason such a plane would not be expected to be a crystal face; the actual faces would be expected to be planes populated by both sorts of ions—these being the ones having the least attracting forces (the most self-satisfied planes, so to speak), and therefore the ones with the lowest rate of thickening. In the caesium bromide structure it so happens that the rhombic dodecahedral surfaces are not only populated by equal numbers of both sorts of ions, but are also the most densely packed; and this is usually so—it is unlikely that planes containing only one sort of ion would be the most closely packed, because, in the nature of things, ions of like charge tend to keep away from each other in the structure.

The same situation is found in sodium chloride and the many crystals having this type of arrangement. The planes containing only one sort of ion, which in this structure are the octahedral planes, have a high rate of thickening and are *not* the natural bounding faces. The faces actually found are cube faces, which are populated with equal numbers of positive and negative ions; again these are also the most densely packed, but it should not be assumed that it is the plane packing density that settles the matter; it is more likely that the distribution of electric charges is the principal influence. (Octahedral faces can be caused to appear if certain other substances like urea are put in the solution from which crystals are growing; but that is another story.)

In molecular crystals like benzene, there are no strong electric charges to consider, and the faces of the crystals are very often those planes in which there is the densest packing of molecules. For crystals having only one molecule to the unit cell, the faces may actually be parallel to the sides of the unit cell. This is natural, because in choosing the unit cell one usually accepts the unit with the shortest edges and with angles nearest to right angles, and the faces of such a cell would be likely to be the planes most densely packed with molecules. This is certainly true for hexamethylbenzene (see Fig. 26b). But where there is more than one molecule in the unit cell, the planes most densely packed with molecules are not likely to be faces of the unit cell, so the crystal faces are usually inclined to the unit cell edges: in benzene itself the molecules are arranged in a manner something like the face-centered cubic structure (though it is not actually cubic but orthorhombic), and so it is not surprising to find that the crystals are something like octahedra in shape (Fig. 29), for the octahedral planes are the most densely packed with molecules.

FIG. 29.   Crystals of benzene are octahedral in shape. The molecules, which are shaped like round cushions, are arranged in a face-centered manner.

The examples chosen to illustrate this chapter have been particularly simple ones, and in these it is possible to see the way in which denseness of packing of planes ("reticular density" —network density—as it is sometimes called) settles which faces the crystal shall have. But in many crystals it would be difficult to decide which are the planes most densely packed with molecules or ions; in fact, in many crystals no plane is really close-packed in the sense of presenting a well-filled surface without large hollows: wherever one takes a cut through the crystal (subject to the rule that molecules or ions must be kept intact and either left in the surface or taken away bodily), there are always hollows large enough to take nearly half a molecule or ion each, and thus capable of attracting new molecules to

form new layers easily. Besides, there is the shape of the molecules
to consider: some of them have cobbled surfaces or even good-
sized hollows, which would be just as effective in attracting
fresh material for growth as the hollows *between* molecules. In
such crystals it is difficult to define denseness of surface packing
in a precise way, and consequently it is not possible to say what
determines which faces the crystal will have. Presumably the
breadth and depth of the hollows in relation to the size of the
particles has something to do with it; but it is doubtful whether
it would be worth while to try to develop a quantitative theory
on these lines, because it is really intermolecular forces which
settle such matters, and the geometrical approach by way of the
concept of reticular density in a plane or of the topography of
the surface can only be expected to be an effective substitute
in particularly simple cases.

There is another important aspect of crystal shape which is
of great interest: what is it that settles the relative dimensions in
different directions? Why are some crystals "chunky" (i.e.,
much the same thickness in all directions), while others are
flat plates and yet others thin needles? The shape depends, of
course, on the relative rates of growth in the different directions.
Often it is pretty clear that the general shape is settled by the
relative strengths of the forces holding the particles together in
the different directions. A good example is the substance known
as urea. This, one of the simplest substances containing all the
four elements, carbon, nitrogen, oxygen, and hydrogen, is the
principal final product of nitrogen metabolism in mammals; it
is formed in the decomposition of proteins, and is excreted in
urine. Synthetic urea is used for making plastics (urea formal-
dehyde resins) and in agriculture as a fertilizer. The crystals
usually grow as long rodlike prisms with the interesting shape
shown in Fig. 30. Molecules of urea are Y-shaped objects with
the leg of the Y along the needle direction (Fig. 30), and it is
known that there are strong electrical attractions between the
top of one Y and the bottom of the next—they are of the same
nature as the attractions in ice between hydrogens of one molecule
and oxygens of the next (what the chemist calls "hydrogen

bonds"). Consequently it is not surprising that the rate of addition of molecules is greater along the direction of these attractions than along any of the sideways directions where the forces between the molecules are much weaker; hence the needle shape. The arrangement of molecules, which is not shown in detail but is suggested in the sketch, also shows why the crystals have the curious shape with the top gable at right angles to the bottom gable.

Strong forces in two directions in a plane, with weaker forces at right angles to it, lead to the growth of flat platelike crystals. An outstanding example is graphite, the soft form of carbon used in "lead" pencils; atoms of carbon are joined in honeycomb

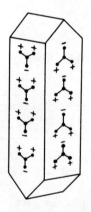

FIG. 30.   Urea crystals are elongated because strong electrical attractions lead to rapid growth in one direction.

fashion in sheets by the very strong forces which hold atoms together in molecules (Fig. 24), while the sheets are held together in the crystal only by the comparatively weak forces between separate molecules, consequently the crystals grow as thin plates, which slide off the pencil point and on to the paper as we write. (The column in the lead pencil is *not* a natural form of graphite but a manufactured one.)

Needlelike or platelike crystal shapes are, however, not always due to marked differences in the forces of attraction in the different directions; some crystals in which the forces of attraction between individual atoms in neighboring molecules seem to be much the same in all directions grow nevertheless in the nonchunky shapes. In these crystals it is often noticeable that the molecules also have nonchunky shapes; *but* the shape of the crystal does not correspond to the shape of the molecule—needleshaped molecules tend to form platelike crystals with the long molecules standing perpendicular to the plate, and flat molecules tend to form needlelike crystals with the needle direction perpendicular to the plane of the molecules (Fig. 31a). The reason seems to be some-

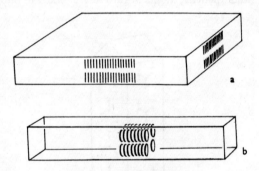

FIG. 31. (a) Long molecules, packed parallel, give platelike crystals, while (b) flat molecules, packed parallel, give needlelike crystals.

thing like this: long molecules pack parallel like a bundle of sticks with the ends all level, and additional molecules can add on to the side of the bundle quite quickly; there is no difficulty in starting new layers because, once a molecule settles, it is held by attractive forces all along its length and is not likely to escape again. But the starting of a new layer on the end of the bundle (that is, on the big flat face of the platelike crystal) is much less likely. We can imagine that molecules in the liquid are unlikely to come in contact, correctly oriented, with the ends of the bundless—they are only too likely to be sideways-on instead of end-on, as they are required to be to form a new layer; and even if some of them do manage to balance end-on for a moment, they are very likely to be hustled off again before they manage to attract enough companions to set up a stable new layer; there is very little to hold them in such a position, only the forces between the small ends of the molecules. It looks as if we could only expect to get crystals one molecular layer in thickness.

But crystals of such substances, though thin, are not as thin as all that; what happens is that "dislocations" occur—the exceedingly thin plates are so fragile that they tend to bend and distort and tear under their own weight, and if a crystal half tears, it exposes edges on which fresh liquid molecules can settle and start off spiral growths. This is what happened in the early stages of the growth of the paraffin crystal shown in Plate 5; the paraffin molecules, which are thirty times as long as they are thick, stand perpendicular to the plate. If it were not for the occurrence of dislocations, the crystals would be so thin that we should not be able to see them except with very special arrangements; as it is, they do grow into plates which, though thin and fragile, can at any rate be seen and handled.

Flat molecules, for similar reasons, can pile up on each other rapidly (it is like piling coins in columns), but addition edge-on is much slower; the net forces holding new molecules edge-on to the pile are so small that any that do settle are likely to be pushed off again by energetic liquid molecules incorrectly oriented, so new layers have little chance of persisting. In other words, the rate of growth in the edge direction of the molecules is much less than in the direction perpendicular to their planes, and so the crystal becomes a long needle, as in Fig. 31b. Maybe dislocations help sideways growth in such crystals, but as far as I know they have not yet been observed.

These neat reciprocal relations between molecular shape and crystal shape (flat molecules in long crystals and long molecules in flat crystals) only occur when the molecules all pack parallel. This very often happens with long molecules. However, flat molecules do not always arrange themselves simply like parallel piles of coins; more often than not, they pack in a zigzag fashion as in coronene (Fig. 32). The growth of this crystal is slow in the direction in which pure edgewise deposition must take place (out from the paper in the diagram), rapid in the left-and-right direction, and moderate in the up-and-down direction where deposition is not edgewise but half-and-half—there is enough of a step for a new molecule to sit on with fair comfort. This results in a lath-shaped crystal. But the relative dimensions of crystals having this type of structure depend very much on the angle of the zigzag packing pattern (as well as on the relative dimensions of the molecules), for this is what settles the widths of the steps for new molecules to sit down on. Notice that for such structures flat molecules may give flat crystals, but the flat plane of the molecule is *not* parallel to the plane of the crystal.

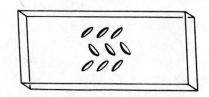

Fig. 32: The structure and crystal shape of coronene.

For crystals with more complex structures, with molecules in several different orientations, and for those in which there are both molecular shape effects *and* differences of forces in different directions, it becomes much more difficult to make any generalizations or to predict even roughly what the shape will be. We must admit that we do not know enough about the forces controlling growth to be able to understand the known shapes of such crystals, let alone to predict the shapes from the structure.

One final word. Any crystal of cubic symmetry, however complicated the molecular packing scheme (with many molecules in different orientations), and whatever the shape of the molecules, must be "chunky" in shape, provided that it is not skeletal and provided also that it grows in uniform surroundings. If it grows in the ordinary way with flat faces, the cubic structure means that there are bound to be several faces all exactly equivalent in structure and with the same chances of growth, oriented around the structure so that they form a solid "chunky" shape. Needles and plates cannot occur. If a cubic crystal grows in skeletal fashion, there must be several main arms—usually six or eight—radiating in space; flat skeletons are not possible for cubic crystals (provided that opportunities for growth are equal all around). If needles or plates or flat skeletons are found, it means that opportunities for growth in the different directions were very unequal.

CHAPTER 6

Symphony of Shapes

To many people, the most enigmatic aspect of crystals is their symmetry of shape. It is surprising enough to find stones with perfectly flat mirrorlike surfaces; but it seems still more extraordinary that "dead" matter assumes regular and sometimes highly symmetrical shapes. There is an engraving by Dürer called "Melancholia" which depicts a brooding figure surrounded by various natural objects, one of which—occupying a good part of the foreground—is a solid object like an enormous crystal; the figure is perhaps contemplating the mysteries of nature, and it seems appropriate that a prominent place is occupied by a crystal shape, challenging the human onlooker by the enigma of the precision and symmetry of its form. (I do not see, by the way, why the contemplation of the mysteries of nature should be associated with "melancholia"; delight and fascination seem more appropriate reactions. Perhaps Dürer's attitude to natural phenomena was very different from ours; or is there some quite different meaning in the picture?)

We may admit that the sort of symmetry found in crystals is more austere—more "dead," if you like—than the symmetry of a flower or a tree, and considerably less subtle than what we call symmetry or balance in a picture or a symphony. Living organisms on the scale of complexity of plants can have grace and beauty of form arising from freedom of variation within a complex structural scheme which does not insist on straight lines; and in works of art, men aim at creating forms which have something of the subtlety, the freedom within a self-consistent scheme, and the lack of rigidity we associate with life. The forms of crystals, with their straight lines and precise symmetries, are of an altogether simpler type, and it seems in a way appropriate that "dead" matter should show a cruder, more rigid type of symmetry than living organisms. Crystal forms may seem at first enigmatic, but they are at any rate much less subtle than the forms of living organisms; the precision and symmetry of form, which seem at first so extraordinary, are really evidences of an essentially simple type of internal organization. We know that the internal organization is of the most primitive kind—an exact repetition (a vast number of times and always in straight lines) of the same pattern unit of atoms; a primitive kind of organization which contrasts strongly with the complexity and differentiation of parts in living organisms.

But if crystal forms are, from the artistic point of view, essentially primitive, they have at any rate some of the aesthetic attractions of the primitive: in contemplating these elemental shapes, we are close to the fundamentals of form, and in trying to understand the principles of their structure we are learning something about the nature of space—something about the world we live in. Our mental reactions to crystal forms have something in common with our impressions of Stonehenge or the Pyramids of Egypt (the aesthetic impact of which owes its tremendous force to their very crudity and simplicity) and something in common with our attitude to the austerities of pure mathematics.

One of the principal features of crystal form which strikes us as primitive is the straight-line scheme—the plane faces, straight edges, and sharp corners. These features, of course, result from the straight-line character of the fundamental atomic pattern: all the units of structure are packed in ranks upon ranks, always in straight lines, and repeated monotonously without variation (except for "accidental" imperfections) in all directions in space. Why this relentless rigidity of straight lines? The answer is that a straight-line scheme is the only way of carrying on an exact repetition of the same unit of pattern in all directions. You will remember from Chapter 2 that the formation of a repeating pattern is the result of a tendency for the structural units to attain whatever arrangement has the least free energy; this one particular arrangement is accordingly set up everywhere. Each pattern unit has to have the same relation to neighboring pattern units, everywhere in the pattern, and the only way of achieving this is to follow a straight-line scheme. This is true even on a flat surface. Suppose we start with a simple type of pattern unit and decide that the relation between unit *1* and its neighbors shall be as in Fig. 33a, with motif *2* tilted over a little. Now try

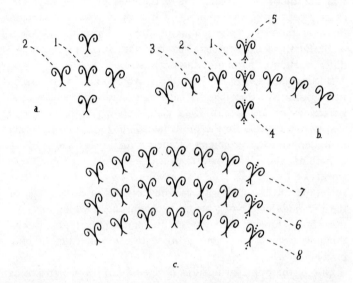

FIG. 33. It is not possible to make a truly repeating pattern based on a curved framework. (a) Starting with an arrangement in which motif *2* is tilted with respect to motif *1*; (b) repetition of the *1-2* sequence leads to the curved line *1, 2, 3, ...*; (c) similar repetition starting from *4* and *5* leads to this curved arrangement, but since the relation of *6* to *7* and *8* is different from that of *1* to *4* and *5*, the arrangement is not a repeating pattern.

extending it; the relation of *3* to *2* has to be the same as that of *2* to *1*—in other words, *3* has to be tilted over a little more; and the extension of this line of units leads to the curved line in diagram (b). So far, so good; but now put in the other curved lines of units as in (c); there is already something wrong even after so few repetitions, for the relation of *6* to *7* and *8* is not the same as that of *1* to *4* and *5*—the central lines of *6, 7* and *8* are not in line with each other. If these motifs were molecules which fit well when placed as in diagram (a), they would not fit at all well in arrangement (c); and the further you go with the pattern, the worse it gets, for we should find the lines running into each other. This is true for any curved scheme; try it for yourself on a piece of paper.

You may say that in wallpapers and dress materials there are often curves; but you will find that a curve never continues in the same direction—it veers back and forth as in Fig. 34, always returning to the general straight line direction. The curves are merely details of the pattern unit; each pattern unit consists of two motifs joined by the curved line, and the succession of pattern units (dotted-line areas) follows a strict straight line.

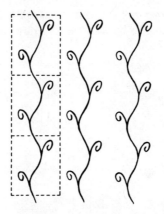

FIG. 34. Repeating patterns can have curves in each pattern unit, but the succession of pattern units is based on a strict straight-line scheme.

What is true on a flat surface is equally true in space; meandering and helical (coil-like) patterns are found in many crystals, but not one-way curves. A one way curve can only persist for a short distance, in normal circumstances. Large-scale curves *are* sometimes found, as in ice patterns on window panes; but these arise from the intervention of distorting forces (variations in the glass surface, minute deposits of other substances on the

glass, and surface tension effects in the water) which, so to
speak, defeat the crystal's attempt at straight lines and pull it
out of shape. Curves are not natural to crystals: the straightline
scheme is an essential feature of their primitive repetitive type
of organization.

Crystal forms may be primitive in the artistic sense, but they
are not all simple in the sense of being easy to grasp mentally.
Some of them, like cubes and simple prisms, are straightforward
enough, but others are likely to tax all our powers of observation
in our attempts to grasp the principles on which they are based.
The type of organization in crystal structures may be primitive
in the extreme when compared with that of living matter, but
even primitive types of structure can give rise to the most
fascinating complexities of shape. Consider the crystal shown in
Fig. 35, for example; how are we to grasp the essentials of its

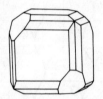

FIG. 35.   A crystal of sodium chlorate.

form and become conscious of the principles of its symmetry?
From the main faces, it looks as if the crystal is trying to be a
cube, but the little faces on the edges and corners spoil the
symmetry; yet there is something regular about it—these little
faces are not haphazard. Of course, it is easier when handling
an actual solid crystal instead of looking at a mere picture on a
page; but even when one has a real crystal to turn about and
examine from different points of view, it is not always easy to
make out the principles of its from. When there are many facets,
it may be difficult to decide which of them are to be regarded
as being of essentially the same type, and which to separate
mentally as belonging to different types. This is the sort of

problem which faced those who, two centuries ago, first started studying crystals seriously.

Their problems were the more difficult because different crystals of the same substance, even those in the same batch, are usually not all exactly the same shape: the relative sizes of the faces vary considerably. This, as we have seen in the previous chapters, is due to the accidents of growth. (There is more about it in Chapter 7.) There are two ways of getting over the possible confusion due to such causes: one is to look at a number of crystals in the same batch and so form a general idea of the shape by mentally averaging out the variations; the other arises from the fact that, however much the relative sizes of the faces vary, the angles between them are constant to a high degree of precision. This became evident as soon as instruments were devised to measure the angles. At first, two straight edges hinged together were used to make contact with a pair of crystal faces, the angle between them being afterwards read off. But later a much more accurate method, based on the reflection of light, was introduced, and is still in use today: the crystal is mounted on a rotatable stem (see Fig. 36), turned until a small distant light is seen reflected in one face, and then turned again until another face comes into the reflecting position, the angle between the two positions then being read off. The instrument that does this is known as a goniometer.

The reason why the angles between crystal faces are so remarkably constant is that the surfaces are related to the internal structure—the different faces are different simple ways of finishing off the stacking scheme, and the stacking scheme is extremely precise and usually invariable. By focusing attention on the angles between faces, we are getting away from the imperfections due to the accidents of growth, and are coming to grips with the ideal symmetry—the symmetry of the internal structure. It is not my intention to describe here the procedure by which crystallographers deal systematically with a set of angular measurements; it will be sufficient to say that a set of angles does settle any doubts as to which faces are to be regarded as similarly related to the stacking pattern and which are to be mentally separated as different types. And when this is done, the best way to start thinking about the symmetry of the crystal is to replace the actual crystal by an idealized picture in which similar faces all have the same size and shape. Line drawings of crystals in books on mineralogy and crystallography are very often of this idealized type, in which inequalities due to the accidents of growth are removed.

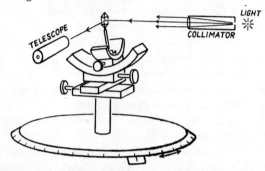

Fig. 36. Principle of the reflecting goniometer. The adjusting head comprises two mutually perpendicular arc movements and two cross movements.

Before going any further we should be quite clear about the meaning of the word "symmetry." When we say that a pair of semidetached houses is a symmetrical building, we mean that one half of it is exactly equivalent to the other half—not identical, but equivalent in the sense that one's left hand is equivalent to one's right—and further, that the two halves are precisely placed so that one is like the mirror image of the other (Fig. 37). This sort of symmetry is often found in crystals; one which has it is ammonium sulfate. It is the type of symmetry known as a "plane of symmetry": we can imagine a plane going right through the middle of the crystal (or the pair of semidetached houses) and acting as a mirror which, so to speak, converts one half into the other.

But mirror symmetry is not the only type of symmetry. Think of a tram, for instance (Fig. 38); one half of it is not like the reflection of the other half—it is not merely a mirror equivalent, but is identical with the other half; and what we have to do in imagination to convert one half into the other is not to reflect it in a mirror but simply to turn it round bodily through half a

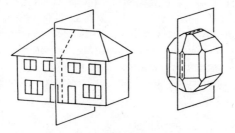

FIG. 37. A pair of semidetached houses has a plane of symmetry. So has a crystal of ammonium sulfate.

complete revolution, the axis being an imaginary vertical line through the center of the tram. This sort of symmetry is also very frequently found in crystals (cane sugar, for example, in Fig. 38), and objects like this are said to have an "axis of twofold symmetry."

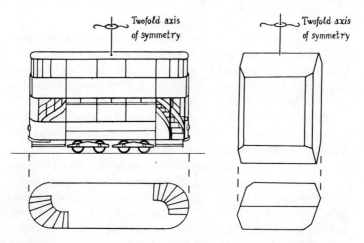

FIG. 38. A tram has an axis of twofold symmetry. A crystal of cane sugar has the same type of symmetry.

In a tram the axis of symmetry relates one *half* of the tram to the other; but in objects having rotation symmetry it is not always halves that are identical—sometimes there are three or more parts which are related in this way. The three-legged device on the arms of the Isle of Man (Fig. 39) is a perfect example of threefold rotation symmetry: the three legs are identical, and to move one of them into the position of the next, it has to be turned through one-third of a revolution. Threefold rotation symmetry is also found in crystals; a good example is shown in Fig. 39.

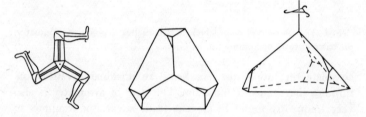

Fig. 39.   The axis of threefold symmetry, in the arms of the Isle of Man (*left*) and in a crystal of sodium periodate trihydrate (*center* and *right*).

Fourfold and sixfold rotation symmetry are found not infrequently in everyday objects: square tables having a fourfold axis of symmetry are sometimes seen, and many "lead" pencils have the shape of a hexagonal prism. Fivefold symmetry is far less common in manufactured articles, but many flowers have five similar petals and a fivefold axis of symmetry. This, however, is where crystals part company with other natural objects, for fivefold symmetry axes are never found in crystals. Some crystals are known in which the faces have a pentagonal shape, like the pyrites crystal in Fig. 40, but the pentagons are not regular (the angles are not all equal), and it is only individual faces which have this shape; the crystal as a whole does not possess any fivefold axis of symmetry. Four- and sixfold axes of symmetry are common in crystals, but fivefold axes are not found at all. In fact, the only axes of symmetry found in crystals are those already mentioned—twofold, threefold, fourfold and sixfold; there are no others. Among all the hundreds of minerals and the thousands of laboratory-made substances, no crystal species have ever been found which show fivefold, sevenfold, eightfold, or any higher symmetry.

This is surely a remarkable fact; if external shape were the only consideration, there is no reason why fivefold or higher-than-sixfold symmetry should not exist; it is quite easy to construct solid shapes having such symmetries—in fact, there are many regular solid figures known to mathematicians which are never exhibited by crystals. The generalization that two-, three-, four-, and sixfold symmetry axes are the only ones ever found in crystals is so striking that one naturally looks for some fundamental significance in it. The clue is, of course, that external shape is certainly not the only consideration. The inside of a crystal is not just a featureless mass which can be bounded by any

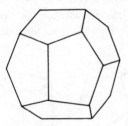

Fig. 40. A crystal of iron pyrites, FeS_2. The faces are not regular pentagons, and the crystal does not have fivefold symmetry.

surfaces whatever; it has a precise structure which is a repetition of solid pattern units, and the flat faces owe their existence to the nature of the internal pattern. The only faces that can exist are those which are natural boundaries of a solid pattern made by the repetition of identical units, and the only shape symmetries that can exist are those that conform to the symmetries developed in packing schemes.

In order to think about possible packing schemes, let us imagine that each pattern unit in a crystal is in a little box; it is always possible to partition a three-dimensional pattern into a number of identical boxes, just as a two-dimensional pattern on a wallpaper or a textile fabric can be divided into a number of identical areas. Having put the pattern units into little boxes, we can now think what shapes of boxes can be packed so as to fill space without leaving any holes between them. It will be found that not all types of boxes can be packed properly: only for certain shapes is it possible. There is no need to go off and make little cardboard boxes to see which ones pack properly; for if we think of just one layer (and we are justified in doing this because the other layers are bound to be exactly the same), we are reducing the problem to a two-dimensional one which can be solved by drawing diagrams on paper or by looking at wallpaper or textile patterns. It is found that squares, rectangles, nonrectangular parallelograms, and regular hexagons pack perfectly, but regular pentagons cannot pack properly—nor can heptagons or any greater-than-six-sided figures. If you try drawing them in contact to fill up the area without leaving space, as in Fig. 41, you find that the thing cannot

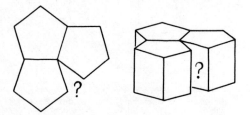

FIG. 41. Regular pentagons cannot pack without leaving spaces. This is why fivefold axes of symmetry do not occur in crystals.

be done; and if it cannot be done on a flat surface, it cannot be done in space. The only types of unit area possible in repeating patterns on a flat surface are those with two-, three-, four-, and sixfold rotation symmetry, and likewise in space the only possible types of boxlike unit volumes are those having these same symmetries. This is evidently the reason why five- or greater-than-sixfold symmetries are not found in crystals. It is in the nature of things—it is one of the inevitabilities of geometry—not at first sight a very obvious one, but convincing enough as soon as you try it out.

There is one other type of symmetry which is very common in crystals, the type known as centrosymmetry. Think of the letter S; if you start out from the center in any direction, you come to the same result as if you started out in the diametrically opposite direction (see Fig. 42). This is the essence of centro-symmetry; but the letter S is not an entirely convincing example, because it can equally well be said to have a twofold *axis* of symmetry, and so it is not evident that the center of symmetry is a new type that can exist in its own right. For shapes on flat surfaces there is really no need to drag in centrosymmetry at all; but in three dimensions centrosymmetry *can* exist in its own right. There is no really convincing example among everyday objects, and the nearest we can get is a camera set up to photo-graph a picture the same size as the original (see Fig. 42). The

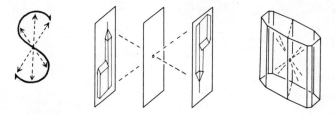

FIG. 42. Centrosymmetry. *Left:* In the letter S. *Center:* When a camera takes a photograph of a picture the same size, the lens or pinhole is a center of symmetry. *Right:* A crystal of hydrated copper sulfate (the familiar blue substance used as a fungicide); one half of the crystal is like a pinhole photograph of the other side.

image produced by the lens is not only reversed right and left, but is also upside down with respect to the original, and in this way the relation between object and image differs from both rotation symmetry and mirror symmetry; in fact the only way of describing the relation is as centrosymmetry. The relation does not, by the way, depend on any peculiar properties of the lens; the situation would be just the same if there was a small pinhole instead of the lens. In fact, perhaps the best way of thinking of centrosymmetry in a crystal such as that of hydrated copper sulfate shown in Fig. 42 is to imagine a small pinhole at the center. Just as we imagined a mirror replacing the dividing wall of a pair of semidetached houses, converting one-half into the other, so we can imagine a pinhole at the center of the crystal, taking a pinhole photograph of one half which proves to be identical with the other half and exactly superposed on it; the pinhole, in fact, is what we mean by a center of symmetry.

The list of types of symmetry that can exist in crystal shapes is quite short; in fact, we have nearly completed it. The only other type is perhaps best appreciated by thinking once more about the crystal of urea, which grows as long prisms finished off at each end, not with a pyramid, but with a gable—and the gable at one end is at right angles to the one at the other end (Fig. 43).

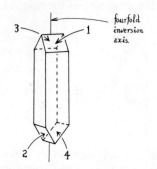

FIG. 43.   The crystal of urea has a fourfold inversion axis of symmetry.

A gable rather than a pyramid indicates only a twofold rotation axis of symmetry; but there is more to it than that, for it is found that all four gable faces are at *exactly* the same angle to the prism faces, and the top gable is rotated *exactly* 90° with respect to the other. All four faces are equivalent, and so it is evident that the urea crystal has a special kind of fourfold symmetry axis. This is called the tetragonal inversion axis: to go from one gable face to the others, you rotate the prism

axis through a right angle and at the same time invert through
the crystal center; this takes you alternately from a top face to
a bottom face. Other types of inversion axes sometimes found
in crystals are threefold and sixfold inversion axes, and with
these the list of symmetry elements that are possible in crystal
shapes is complete. (There is no need for any mention of a
twofold inversion axis, because it is nothing more nor less than
a plane of symmetry.)

It is comforting that the list of different types of symmetry
("symmetry elements") which can be found in crystal shapes is
so short—mirror symmetry, two-, three-, four-, and sixfold
rotation symmetry (not forgetting the inversion axes), and
centrosymmetry. The prospect of looking for symmetries becomes
less bewildering when we know that so few different types are
possible. However, we soon find, when we try to analyze shapes
to see what symmetry they possess, that many of them do not
possess just one type of symmetry, but have several symmetry
elements. In fact, we can, if we like, regard the more highly
symmetrical shapes as being created by various combinations of
the basic symmetry elements. Take a square table, for instance:
not only does it have a fourfold rotation axis vertical through
its center (Fig. 44), but it also has two planes of symmetry through
the center and parallel to the sides, and another set of two planes
of symmetry diagonally placed. And a cubic crystal has even

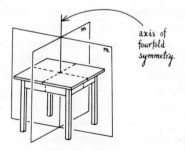

FIG. 44.   A square table has planes of symmetry (*m* for mirror),
as well as a fourfold rotation axis. (It also has diagonal planes of symmetry.)

more symmetry elements; it has not only the planes and fourfold
axes just mentioned, repeated for the side faces as well as the
top, but also twofold axes through all the edges, a set of threefold
axes through the corners, and a center of symmetry in the middle
(see Fig. 45).

As the number of different symmetry elements is so small, it
is not a very formidable task to think of all the possible combinations of them. Crystallographers and mineralogists did this in
the last century, and found that the number of different combinations is thirty-two. Experience has confirmed that all crystal

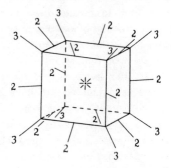

Fig. 45. A cubic crystal has a center of symmetry, twelve twofold
axes, and four threefold axes of symmetry. (It also has several planes of
symmetry.)

shapes belong to one or other of these thirty-two symmetry
types; no further ones have been found. As a matter of fact,
there is still one of the theoretically possible symmetry types
of which no certain examples are known; no fundamental
significance is attached to this, and it may be that examples will
eventually turn up.

Remember that the number thirty-two refers to symmetry
types; actual shapes are of course infinite in variety, for each
symmetry type can include many different shapes. Consider the
most highly symmetrical type—that of which the cube is the
most familiar example. The cube is not the only shape which
has this combination of symmetry elements; there are many

other shapes which, though they look at first sight very different
from the cube, have precisely the same set of symmetry elements.
A few examples are shown in Fig. 46: the octahedron, the characteristic shape of alum crystals, is one; and the still more fascinating
rhombic dodecahedron, the shape of garnets, with its twelve
"diamond-shaped" faces, is another. The faces of these are of
quite different types from those of the cube—they are quite
different finishing-off surfaces for the fundamental cubic patterns
of the internal structures—but the symmetries are identical.
Many crystals are known which have various combinations of
these types of faces (an example is shown in Fig. 46), and these
too have the full set of symmetry elements.

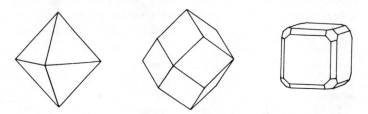

FIG. 46. An alum crystal (an octahedron), a garnet (a rhombic
dodecahedron), and a crystal of cuprite, which has small octahedral
faces on the corners and small dodecahedral faces on the edges of the
basic cube. All these shapes have the same symmetries as the cube.

All these highly symmetrical crystals are based on cubic
pattern units: if the structure is divided up into identical pattern
units in the simplest possible way, the shape of the pattern unit
("unit cell") is a precise cube. (The size of the cubic pattern
unit is different for each substance, but we are not concerned
with that for the moment; we are concerned only with the shape
and symmetry.) But not all crystals having exactly cubic unit
cells possess all the symmetries enumerated earlier as those of
a cube; the reason is that the arrangement of atoms (or molecules
or ions) in an exactly cubic unit cell need not possess the full
set of symmetries. The shape of a crystal depends, as we have
seen, on the relative rates of growth of the various faces: those

having the slowest rates of growth dominate the shape. The rates of growth of the various faces depend on the details of the space arrangement of molecules, because this is what decides the molecular pattern on each face, and thus the forces of attraction between the faces and the approaching molecules. This is why the shape symmetry of a crystal is often a good indication of the symmetry of arrangement of the molecules; the information it gives goes beyond the shape of the unit cell, and tells us something about the arrangement inside the unit cell. Sodium chlorate (a substance much used as a weed killer on garden paths) is a good example; the crystals, if they are grown in such a way as to develop the various little facets as well as the main cube faces, show only twofold, not fourfold, rotation symmetry; and, in addition, they have no planes of symmetry, nor a center of symmetry (see Fig. 34). The precise arrangement of atoms in crystals of sodium chlorate is known (it has been deduced by the X-ray methods which are the subject of a later chapter), and it does indeed have the symmetries suggested by the shape of the crystal.

Perhaps the most surprising crystal shape to find in the cubic system is the pentagonal dodecahedron, shown in Fig. 40; this is the shape sometimes assumed by the mineral pyrites, iron disulfide—a solid figure with twelve equal five-sided faces. It does seem very odd to find five-sided faces on a crystal having a cubic unit cell; but this is not a contradiction of what was said before about the impossibility of fivefold symmetry in crystals, for the faces are not regular pentagons, and the crystal as a whole does not have fivefold symmetry. It has the four threefold axes which are the hallmark of the cubic system—the only set of symmetry elements possessed by *all* cubic crystals; it has twofold axes like sodium chlorate (again no fourfold ones), but differs from sodium chlorate in having three planes of symmetry.

Five of the thirty-two symmetry types have cubic unit cells. In a similar way the other symmetry types can be classified according to the type of shape of the unit cell. Seven of them have tetragonal unit cells—rectangular boxes with a square base but a height which has a different length from the base edge (and the ratio of the height to the base edge is different for each substance crystallizing in this form).

One crystal which has the full symmetry possible in this group is ammonium dihydrogen phosphate (a substance used in agriculture as a fertilizer), which grows in long square prisms finished off at each end with a pyramid; another of the same type, but having additional facets, is titanium dioxide, the mineral rutile; a more squat type is tin oxide, the mineral cassiterite; all of these are shown in Fig. 47. A fascinating example with a lower degree of symmetry is urea, illustrated a little way back (Fig. 43). The structural basis for this sort of shape symmetry is quite clear from the molecular arrangement; half the Y-shaped molecules are right way up, and the other half upside down but at the same time at right angles to the first set. The fourfold inversion axis in the arrangement of molecules is manifested by the shape of the crystal.

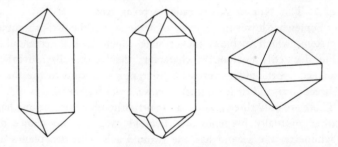

FIG. 47. Tetragonal crystals. *Left:* ammonium dihydrogen phosphate; *center:* rutile (titanium dioxide); *right:* cassiterite (tin oxide).

Inversion axes (sometimes called alternating axes) are also found in crystals which have a single threefold axis. Look, for example, at the calcite crystal in Fig. 48; the three faces at each pyramidal end are all equivalent in the sense that they all make the same angle with the prism faces, but the bottom set of three is twisted 60° to the top set. All six faces can be accounted for by a single symmetry operation in which, at each step, a rotation of 120° (one-third of a revolution) combined with inversion through the center is performed; another way of doing it would be to rotate 60° (one-sixth of a revolution) at each step and reflect in the equatorial plane. Should this be called a threefold axis or a kind of sixfold axis? It is a matter of taste, but the accepted convention among crystallographers is to think in terms of the first description, which involves inversion rather than reflection, and to call it a threefold inversion axis. This sort of thing means that the trigonal and hexagonal systems of crystals overlap to some extent. Some crystals, like the one in Fig. 39, are undoubtedly only trigonal in symmetry, while others, like iodoform (Fig. 48), undoubtedly have full sixfold symmetry, but there are several types which leave room for differences of opinion. The safest course is to lump them all together in a single system, and so avoid argument; there are no less than twelve symmetry classes which belong to this composite trigonal-hexagonal system. A curious type, also shown in Fig. 48, is that of zinc oxide, which has a proper sixfold axis but dissimilar ends. This type of axis is called a polar axis.

Somewhat lower in the scale of symmetry is the orthorhombic system, which includes the crystals which have a rectangular but decidedly not square character; their unit cells are brick shaped—rectangular, but with different dimensions in the three directions—and their symmetry axes are not higher than twofold. There are only three classes in the orthorhombic system; one has three mutually perpendicular twofold axes and no planes of symmetry, the second has one twofold axis with two planes of symmetry intersecting in it, and the third, the one with the full symmetry possible in this system, has three mutually perpendicular twofold axes and three mutually perpendicular planes of symmetry. An example of the last-mentioned, most highly symmetrical, type is oxalic acid (Fig. 49), a substance much used in metal polishes and rust removers. Another, also shown in this sketch, is lead sulfate.

Three classes have a partly skew character, and are called monoclinic: the three unit cell edges are all unequal in length, and two of them are inclined to each other at an angle which is not a right angle but can have any value (it is different in every different substance), but the third is at right angles to the other two. The three classes which have this sort of unit have either a single twofold axis, a single plane of symmetry, or both (with the twofold axis necessarily perpendicular to the symmetry

FIG. 48.   Crystals of calcite (*left*), iodoform (*center*), and zinc oxide (*right*).

plane). Ordinary cane sugar (shown earlier in Fig. 37) is a good example of the first mentioned type; another is borax (Fig. 50).

The remaining two classes belong to the triclinic system, in which the unit cell is skew in all directions—its three edges are all unequal, and all are inclined to each other at angles which are not right angles. One of the two classes which have this type of unit has a center of symmetry as its only symmetry element (copper sulfate hydrate (Fig. 42) is a good example), and the other of which strontium hydrogen tartrate (Fig. 50) is an

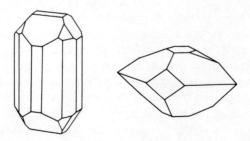

FIG. 49.   Orthorhombic crystals. Lead sulfate (*left*) and oxalic acid (*right*). Three planes of symmetry and three twofold axes.

example, has no symmetry whatever. Is it surprising that any crystal can have *no* symmetry at all? If you are surprised at this, you are probably confusing symmetry with regularity, which is a very different thing. The essential thing about crystals is regularity—the precise repetition of a particular group of atoms, many many times, to form a stack; but the arrangement need not possess any symmetry. It is true that arrangements in crystals usually do possess symmetry of some sort, and crystals without *any* symmetry are very rare; but symmetry is not an essential accompaniment of regularity. Think of a jigsaw puzzle composed of identical but irregular pieces; the pieces fit perfectly, though they have no symmetry.

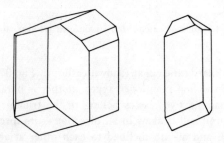

FIG. 50.   *Left:* a monoclinic crystal, borax, which has a twofold axis (nearly perpendicular to the paper) and a plane of symmetry (nearly parallel to the paper). *Right:* a triclinic crystal, strontium hydrogen tartrate, which has no symmetry at all.

The different classes of symmetry are not all equally common in nature; some are quite rare, while others are exceedingly common. Of the highly symmetrical types, certain cubic classes are the most common, because many of the simple salts of inorganic chemistry form cubic crystals. But the highly symmetrical types (cubic, hexagonal, trigonal, and tetragonal) are much less common than some of the less symmetrical ones; in fact, the center of gravity of the crystal kingdom is the monoclinic system, for of the 20,000 crystal species known so far, about half are monoclinic; very many of the complex organic compounds are found in this system. Next in order of plentifulness is the orthorhombic system, which claims about one-quarter of the total. If we add the 15% that are in the triclinic system, this makes 90% of all species in the three systems in the lower half of the symmetry scale, leaving only 10% for the upper half—and the majority of these are cubic.

As far as the *systems* go, then, a rather low degree of symmetry is most common; but if you look at the various symmetry classes within each system, it is a striking fact that it is the highest symmetry class in each system that is most common, by far: in each system, the great majority of known crystals are in the highest symmetry class. We cannot say, then, that nature prefers a fairly low symmetry—as we might have done if we had considered only the main systems; it is not so simple as that. A fairly low symmetry of the *unit cell* seems to be preferred, but the highest symmetry possible on the basis of that unit cell; and so it results that the commonest symmetry *class* of all is the highest class in the monoclinic system—the one with a plane of symmetry as well as a twofold axis. Examples of some of the lower symmetry classes of some of the systems are very rare indeed; these are the crystallographer's curiosities. If he finds one, he is as intrigued and elated as a botanist who discovers a new species of plant with an unusual structure, or a stamp collector who spots a rarity—though his elation is unlikely to find expression in the paper which reports discovery in a scientific journal, for such papers are all too often forbiddingly austere. His feelings are shared only by his laboratory colleagues and by the comparatively few readers dotted about the world who see his article and know enough about the subject to appreciate the point and savor its significance.

There must be some reason for this extreme disparity in the numbers of crystals in the different classes, and the favoring of certain types of symmetry—some reason rooted in the principles of packing of atoms and molecules. It has not yet been explained in any detailed way, but contemplation of these principles does give some hints which point in the right direction, as we shall see in a later chapter.

The complete list of symmetry types consists of six *systems* whose names are based on the shape and symmetry of the *unit cell*—cubic, tetragonal, trigonal plus hexagonal, orthorhombic, monoclinic, and triclinic—and each system comprises two or more *classes* having different combinations of the symmetry elements displayed by the *idealized crystal shape*. The symphony of crystal shapes is in six movements, one of which (the trigonal plus hexagonal) is really two movements telescoped into one; and each movement is in two or more sections.

CHAPTER 7

Variations on Crystal Themes

The symmetries discussed in the last chapter are the symmetries of idealized crystal shapes, in which the accidents of unequal opportunities of growth are ignored. Most real crystals deviate appreciably (or sometimes considerably) from the ideal. In a mass of crystals of the same substance—a group of quartz crystals in a museum, or the many grains of salt or sugar in a handful of either of these substances—it is noticeable that, although all the crystals of any one substance have the same *sort* of shape, they are not all exactly the same. Some quartz crystals may be longer and thinner than others; in some the prism does not have a precisely regular hexagonal cross section like a hexagonal pencil, some of the faces being larger than others; and the terminating pyramid may consist of faces of very different sizes which do not even all meet in a point (though they do usually meet in sharp edges). One obvious possible reason for such variations of shape is that the supply of material for growth was not uniform around the crystals; we can imagine that when a crystal grows from a solution, some faces are more favorably placed than others: faces directly in the path of a flowing solution may receive more deposit of solid material than others which are, so to speak, in a backwater.

The effects of nonuniform surroundings are often displayed in a striking way by crystals grown in the laboratory. Ordinary common salt, for instance, usually forms cubes if the crystals grow in a stirred solution so that they move about; but if crystals grow here and there on the bottom of a dish, they are often found to be square tablets not more than half as thick as they are wide; this is natural enough, because a crystal resting on the bottom can grow upward and sideways but not downward, so that only half-cubes can be expected. As a matter of fact, although crystals in such circumstances cannot actually grow downward, they do make an attempt to preserve their cubic symmetry: it is often found that the under sides are not flat but slightly hollow, with a step formation in the hollow as in Fig. 51. Material has evidently been deposited around the edges of the crystal in such a way as to lift it slightly and gradually; no material reaches the center—and so, with the gradual lifting and the outward growth, the bottom of the crystal becomes hollow. Quite an appreciable force is exerted when matter from the solution squeezes under the edge to lift the crystal, and by putting weights on crystals and finding how much weight is required to prevent the lifting, the forces involved have been measured.

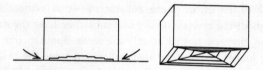

FIG. 51. When a crystal grows on the bottom of a dish, material squeezes in around the edge (*left*), giving a crystal which is slightly hollow on the under side (*right*).

The influence of shortage of supply of solute can often be seen when the growth of crystals is watched in the microscope. If one crystal is well established and another starts growing not far away from it, the part of the new crystal which faces the old one grows more slowly than the rest, and slows down as it approaches the old crystal, evidently because the solution surrounding the old crystal has become somewhat impoverished. Indeed, this can sometimes be confirmed; the strength of a solution of a strongly colored substance is shown by the depth of color—the paler, the weaker; and when such solutions crystallize, it can sometimes be seen that when the growth of a crystal brings one side of it into an impoverished region, growth on that side slows down or stops altogether.

But variations in the rate of growth of different faces of the same crystal are not always due to local impoverishment effects. It is possible by a special optical method to measure accurately the concentration of the solution at any point around a growing crystal, if growth takes place in a thin slice of solution between glass plates; by this method it has been found that sodium chlorate (a substance well known as a weed killer, that happens to be very interesting in many ways to the crystallographer) behaves in a most unexpected manner. Crystals of this substance would grow as cubes in uniform surroundings, but in a thin slice of solution between glass plates they grow as thin plates, approximately square. When the rates of growth of the four faces forming the edges of the plate are followed carefully, it is found that they vary in an irregular manner; sometimes the growth rate of one face slows down to half the rate of the others, or even comes to a complete stop; and this is not due to local impoverishment—it may happen when no other crystal is near. Moreover, measurements show that the solution up against a slow-growing face is often stronger than that against a neighboring face that is growing much faster; and the solution in contact with a stopped face may be much stronger than the solution in contact with the other faces that are still growing. After remaining stationary for a time, a stopped face may suddenly start growing again. Why should a crystal face in contact with strongly supersaturated solution stop growing, and what makes it start growing again?

In Chapter 4 it was mentioned that there are reasons for believing that on some crystals a really perfect crystal face (perfect to an atom) will not grow at all unless the solution in contact with it is strongly supersaturated; new surface nuclei, which are necessary to start new layers, have very little chance of becoming established. It is therefore natural to suppose that when a face of a sodium chlorate crystal stops growing, it is because for some reason or other it has become perfect—there are no incomplete layers, and any imperfections such as dis-locations have become "healed." And when the face starts growing again, this may be due to the result of a miniature earthquake which creates a step which starts a new series of growth layers.

Whatever the explanation of this erratic behavior, there is no doubt about the facts, and we must confess that we cannot predict the rate of growth of an individual crystal face from one minute to the next; the variations from the ideal square plate form when grown between glass plates, or from the ideal cubic form when grown in a bulk of stirred solution, remain unexplained in detail. However, although temporary variations of rate of growth are remarkable enough, over a long period of time the effects on shape are likely to be smoothed out; and it is a fact that sodium chlorate crystals in a batch crystallized material are for the most part not too far from cubic in shape.

What makes some crystals so pleasing to the eye is the existence of small facets that catch the light and flash out reflections when the crystal is moved about; yet other crystals of the same substance are bounded by a very few large faces—often the very minimum number of faces a solid shape can have. Now experience on crystallization under controlled conditions shows that when a crystal grows from a solution in a straightforward way at a constant temperature, it has a simple shape, bounded by very few faces, and it keeps the same faces throughout (they are the slowest-growing faces); but if the temperature is not controlled, so that the crystallizing vessel follows the temperature of the room, warming up during the day and cooling again at night, the crystal may acquire little facets on the edges and corners. Sodium chlorate, a crystal that has already provided us with more than one point of interest, is a good example in this context too. The reason is that when the solution warms up a little, the crystal, which was at first a simple cube, partly redissolves, the edges and corners becoming rounded off; then when the solution cools again, the crystal begins growing and forms little facets on the rounded edges and corners. Growth must not continue for long after this, or the little facets will eliminate themselves again, in the way illustrated earlier in Fig. 28. The process of successive growth and partial redissolving may be repeated more than once; the result is a crystal like the one shown in Fig. 35. Many of the richly faceted crystals obtained when a solution is just left to crystallize without any special controls have been formed in this way; and it is reasonable to suppose that many mineral crystals which display a variety of facets owe their beauties to such fluctuations of growth conditions.

Crystals with a wealth of little facets are not only more fascinating to look at than the simpler types, but are of great value in revealing the inner symmetries. The richly faceted sodium chlorate crystal illustrated in Fig. 35 is less symmetrical than the simple cubes formed in straightforward growth; it indicates that the internal symmetry, which might otherwise have been thought to be the highest possible in the cubic system, is actually of a lower type.

Crystals of certain substances grow always in an elongated form; evidently the arrangement of molecules takes place more rapidly on the ends of the crystal than on the sides. This is a matter of structure: the pattern of molecules on the end faces is different from that on the sides. Either the forces of attraction are stronger along the rod direction than on the sides, as in the urea crystal mentioned in Chapter 5 (Fig. 30), or else the shape of the molecules is such that they can start new layers on the end faces more rapidly than on the sides. Crystals of this sort (sometimes called "acicular," meaning needlelike) usually become longer and thinner when they grow rapidly from strongly supersaturated solution than when they grow slowly (see Plate 3b). This may be a consequence of the fact (illustrated in Fig. 52) that around the end of a rodlike crystal a convergent diffusion flow of material is set up so that the ends are fed better than the sides where diffusion is straightforward and not convergent.

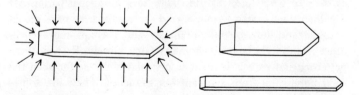

Fig. 52. Convergent diffusion of material around the ends of a long crystal exaggerates the natural difference between the rates of deposition on the ends and on the sides. These are urea crystals, which are much longer and thinner when grown quickly in strongly supersaturated solutions (*bottom, right*) than when grown slowly in slightly supersaturated solutions (*top, right*).

The natural difference between the rates of growth on the ends and on the sides is in this way exaggerated by the diffusion process which is inevitably more convergent around the ends. Another circumstance is that the ends may be in contact with more highly supersaturated solution than the rest of the crystal; the ends, so to speak, stick out further into fresh solution. The crystals in Fig. 52 are of urea, a substance which has already featured in earlier chapters; the crystals grow much longer and thinner in a very strong solution than in a solution that is only just supersaturated.

A shape variation which probably has a similar origin to the one described in the last paragraph and which leads to fascinating and highly decorative forms is due to the tendency of some crystals to form branching growths. Certain substances which, when grown slowly, form solid polyhedral crystals—with the shape, bounded by flat faces, that we tend to think of as a "typical" crystal shape—may in other circumstances grow in branching forms. Some of the most extreme and beautiful variations of this sort are exhibited by ice crystals—not so much the ice crystals formed by the freezing of liquid water, but those which grow from water vapor in the air and descend on us as snowflakes. Under a hand lens a snowflake is seen to consist (usually) of a collection of feathery growths. It is not easy to isolate one individual from the mass (they are all so fragile), but if this could be done, it would be seen that each individual consists of what looks like lacework to a hexagonal pattern. It is evident that, starting from a solid centre, six arms have grown outward and subsequently branched and perhaps rebranched, often retaining hexagonal symmetry fairly closely. Each of these patterned individuals is a single crystal which has forsaken the solid polyhedral from and sent out branches. There are sometimes deviations from strict hexagonal symmetry, but these are no doubt due to variations of conditions around the crystal; on the whole we get the impression that the "natural" form, the one which is built up if conditions around the crystal are uniform, has hexagonal symmetry.

The branching patterns of snowflakes vary enormously. The

fascination of their endless variations led W. A. Bentley to spend years in searching for specimens and recording their beauty on photographic plates. At his home in New England, he took the greatest trouble to get good photographs; his method was to catch snowflakes on a black board and transfer any promising specimens carefully on to a microscope slide; a microscope of quite low power is sufficient for this sort of thing. The results of his patient work were published in a wonderful book containing hundreds of photographs.* A few of these are shown in Plate 6.

All these beautiful shapes are obviously variations on the theme of hexagonal symmetry. But why have the ice crystals forsaken the polyhedral form and taken to branching in this way? A clue is given by experience with other substances, for it is a fact that very strong supersaturation in a solution or a vapor tends to produce branching forms rather than polyhedra, at any rate for some substances. Crystalline substances differ very greatly in their behavior. Some are faithful to the polyhedral form in a great range of conditions, others favor branching forms and can only be persuaded to grow as polyhedra when grown very slowly in very slightly supersaturated solutions; but for those that are versatile, it is strong supersaturation that leads to branching growth (often called by crystallographers "dendritic" growth) and weak supersaturation that favors polyhedral growth. That this is true for ice crystals growing from the vapor, just as it is for salts growing from solution, has been shown by B. J. Mason of London University; he studied the growth of ice crystals at various temperatures and vapor densities, and found that high supersaturation in the vapor favors the beautiful branching forms that are found in natural snowflakes, while at moderate degrees of supersaturation solid polyhedral forms, either hexagonal plates or hexagonal prisms, are produced. The change from one type to the other can be followed by altering the vapor concentration. If a hexagonal plate is growing and then

---

* W. A. Bentley and W. J. Humphries, "Snow Crystals". McGraw-Hill, New York, 1931.

the supersaturation is increased sufficiently, growths are seen to radiate from the corners; after a time they branch, and repeated branching at suitable intervals can produce decorative shapes like those seen in natural snowflakes. The process can indeed be visualized by looking at the series of pictures of snowflakes in Plate 6.

Why does high supersaturation cause a crystal to shoot out at the corners, and why do the corner growths subsequently branch out? One possible reason for the initial breakaway from the hexagonal plate or prism form is that the crystal corners are in contact with more highly supersaturated vapor than the centers of the faces; this is always so for a crystal growing from a vapor or a solution—there is a layer of less concentrated vapor or solution up against the crystal (because some of the material has deposited on the crystal), and the corners stick out further into fresh material than the rest of the crystal. Another is that there is convergent diffusion towards the corners, so that more material arrives there than at the centers of the faces. On both accounts we can expect more rapid growth at the corners, and the excess deposition on the corners would be expected to be greater at the higher supersaturations; the wonder is that most crystals manage to preserve flat faces.

The subsequent branching and often rebranching of the corner growths is more difficult to explain. Of course, the hexagonal symmetry of the arrangement of water molecules in the ice crystal means that there are six directions all exactly equivalent and capable of growing at the same rate if given the chance—if conditions all around the crystal are uniform, all the six corner growths will behave in the same way—but why the repeated branching should take place at the intervals which give us the beautiful patterns of snowflakes, we do not know. This pheno-menon must take its place among many others in nature which, though they might be expected to occur in a uniform manner, in actual fact proceed in an alternating, periodic fashion. There is a hesitation, a buildup of some condition to a critical level, and then a new outbreak; the precise controlling factors are difficult to discover.

Mason's work, which showed that high supersaturation favors fernlike branching growth, also revealed some remarkable facts about the polyhedral growth at the lower levels of supersaturation. The polyhedral crystals are either flat hexagonal plates or else prisms (Fig. 53) but the shape depends on the temperature in a puzzling way. From freezing point down to −3°C, plates are formed; from −3° to −8°C, elongated hexagonal prisms or sometimes hollow prisms; but then from −8° to −12°C, plates again! Below −12°C, fernlike growths are formed if the supersaturation is great enough, but at −16°C, plates again, and below −25°C, prisms again. More variations, and another sort of alternation, just as puzzling as the repeated branching! We do not know the causes of these abrupt changes in the relative rates of growth in the different directions; but knowledge of the facts does help us to understand snowflakes, for by growing crystals at a succession of different temperatures, composite forms like those of natural snowflakes have been obtained. Moreover, it is now possible, by examining snowflakes, to deduce the succession of different temperatures through which the snowflakes moved in their fall to earth. An entertaining piece of scientific detection with beautiful pieces of evidence in more senses than one.

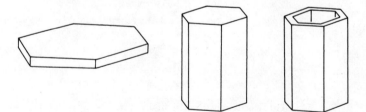

FIG. 53. Shapes of ice crystals formed at low vapor supersaturation.

A substance that is especially addicted to branching growth is ammonium chloride, the principal constituent of the white paste in "dry" batteries. Under ordinary conditions of crystallization from solution, it always grows in the form shown in Plate 3c, with branches at right angles to each other; in fact, it is difficult to get it to do anything else. The branching pattern is rectangular because the arrangement of positive ammonium and negative chloride ions is cubic and the fast growing directions are along the cube axes. The atomic arrangement is the same as that of caesium bromide shown in Fig. 26a, with the ammonium ion (a nitrogen holding four hydrogens) taking the place of caesium, and chlorine taking the place of bromine. Powdered ammonium chloride consists of broken fragments of these delicate branching growths. The photograph, by the way, shows only branching in a plane, but this is only because the substance has crystallized in a thin slice of solution between glass plates; if growth occurs in a bulk of solution, branching occurs in three dimension, giving structures which might be described as resembling rectangular pine trees. Only by letting it crystallize extremely slowly, or by cheating a little and putting a small quantity of manganese chloride or nickel chloride into the solution, can we induce it to form polyhedral crystals—and these are found to have the shape known as the icositetrahedron (Fig. 54), a figure

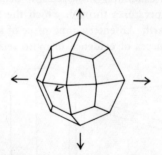

Fig. 54. The icositetrahedron, a figure with 24 sides having the full symmetries of the highest class of the cubic system (an ammonium chloride crystal). The three directions marked are at right angles to each other.

with twenty-four faces having the full symmetries of the highest class of the cubic system. The more usual branching growths can be regarded as originating in icositetrahedra which have shot out at the sharpest corners, which lie on the mutually perpendicular axes (unit cell edges) of the cubic system.

Crystals are sometimes found which are good polyhedra externally, but have internal cavities. A cubic crystal, for instance, may have a set of symmetrically placed cavities inside it, as in Fig. 55a; and I have seen a rhombic dodecahedron of the substance hexamine with twelve perfectly placed cavities inside it as in Fig. 55b. Each cavity lies, so to speak, under a face, and this indicates the origin of such features. At one stage of growth, the center of each face lagged behind the rest, and may indeed have stopped growing while the rest of the face continued to grow; subsequently the hollow which formed in this way closed over to give the cavity. When this happens simultaneously on all the faces, the symmetrically placed set of cavities is the result. The process may be regarded as incipient branching or, if you prefer it, the reverse of branching: instead of shooting out at the corners, growth lags behind at the face centers, possibly because the supersaturation happens to sink to zero, making

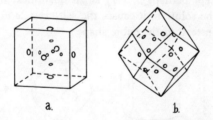

a.   b.

Fig. 55. Crystals with symmetrically placed internal cavities: (a) cubic crystal; (b) rhombic dodecahedron of hexamine.

growth impossible there. It may happen more than once, giving the double set of cavities in Fig. 55a. The first of the snow crystals in Plate 6 (the hexagonal plate crystal) also shows a complex set of internal cavities, due no doubt to similar causes; incidentally the symmetry of the arrangement of cavities is trigonal, not hexagonal—which is odd, because the very branched structures we regard as typical of snowflakes are usually fully hexagonal in symmetry.

The branching forms are the most beautiful and the most spectacular variations of shape, but there is another sort of variation which, though in a sense less extreme, is even more unexpected and may seem at first sight rather mysterious—or at any rate so strange as to need a very special explanation. Ordinary common salt, sodium chloride, usually comes out of solution as simple cubes, but if the solution contains some of the substance called urea (which has already featured for its own sake in other chapters), the salt comes out as modified cubes which have little triangular faces cutting off the corners as in the second picture in Fig. 56. The greater the proportion of urea present, the larger are these corner faces as in the third sketch, and if enough is present, the corner faces are the only ones and the crystal has the shape of a regular octahedron as in the fourth sketch. Now these octahedral crystals have the same composition and structure as the cubic ones—both are just sodium chloride, with equal numbers of sodium ions and chlorine ions arranged in the same cubic fashion. The urea does not enter into the crystals, except perhaps in very small quantities; by just being present in the solution, it causes the salt crystals to grow in the octahedral instead of the cubic shape.

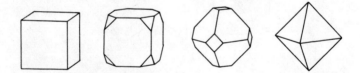

Fig. 56. Common salt grows from pure solution as cubes. The presence of urea in the solution encourages the formation of corner faces; if enough urea is present, the corner faces become the principal ones or even (in the last picture) the only ones.

Many examples of this sort of thing are known. A change exactly opposite to that of sodium chloride is shown by alum, which from pure solution crystallizes as octahedra, but from solutions containing sodium carbonate comes out as cubes. Sometimes remarkably small proportions of dissolved substances produce spectacular changes of shape.

A clue to the way in which the shape-changing substances act suggests itself if one thinks of the rates of growth of the various possible bounding faces of a crystal. We have already seen, in Chapter 5, that the actual bounding faces of a crystal are those which have the *slowest* rate of growth, if by rate of growth we mean the thickness of new solid laid down on each face in a definite time: a state of affairs which may seem at first thought paradoxical, but is certainly demonstrated by the experiment illustrated in Fig. 28, and is indeed a geometrical necessity. Provided always that a polyhedral form is preserved (that is, the crystal does not get out of hand and form branching growths), the bounding faces of crystals are the most slowly growing ones.

This being so, it is clear that the action of urea in promoting the growth of octahedral faces on sodium chloride crystals can be interpreted by saying that urea for some reason changes the relative rates of growth of the cube and octahedron faces, making the octahedral faces the slower of the two. Further, we can speculate that urea may stick strongly to octahedral faces, hindering their growth, but not to cube faces. This would be a beautifully simple explanation of what seemed at first rather mysterious. It is not easy to find evidence to test this idea for the sodium chloride and urea combination, but some crystals whose shape has been changed by the presence of another substance do provide evidence of selective adhesion in this way. For instance, the substance lead nitrate normally grows (from solution in water) as octahedra, but when the solution contains the highly colored dyestuff known as methylene blue, cube faces are produced; and when crystals having both types of faces are examined, it is found that a small quantity of the dyestuff has been trapped in the crystal, but only in those regions which have been built up by deposition on the cube faces (see Fig. 57).

There is a rather spectacular example which supports the idea in a different way. The branching growths of ammonium chloride illustrated in Plate 3c are formed by extremely rapid growth along the three mutually perpendicular directions which are the edges of the cubic unit cell; deposition in the cube face directions is much more rapid than in other directions, when the crystal grows from a pure solution. But if some urea is present in solution, the growth rate in these directions is reduced, and if enough urea is present the crystals formed are cubes, showing that under these conditions the cube faces are the slowest.

The idea of retardation of growth of particular faces by preferential adherence of the impurity is all right as far as it goes, but naturally we should like to know why the impurity sticks to one type of face more than another. Behind every "explanation" there is another question, and we try to push explanations back as far as possible. It is natural to suppose that preferential adhesion has something to do with the great differences between the patterns of atoms on the different types of crystal faces. On cubic crystals there is a square formation on the cube faces, a triangular formation on octahedral faces, and so on, each with a definite spacing. When the dimensions of impurity molecules are known, as well as the dimensions of the atomic patterns on the faces of the crystals concerned, it is sometimes possible to see how an impurity molecule fits better on one type of face than on another. In other cases it seems that it is not the fitting of an isolated impurity molecule, but a group of them, on a crystal face that is responsible for the observed effects. It is a

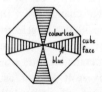

FIG. 57. Section through a crystal of lead nitrate grown in a solution containing methylene blue. Only the regions terminating in cube faces are colored blue.

fact that a group of urea molecules, if arranged as in a crystal of urea (and this is surely the natural way for urea molecules to arrange themselves), would fit nicely on the cube face of an ammonium chloride crystal but not on other types of faces; and in confirmation of this idea, it is found that if urea solution crystallizes on a cubic ammonium chloride crystal, the urea crystals are oriented on the ammonium chloride crystal (Fig. 58) in exactly the way we should expect from the fitting of the atomic patterns.

Our variations become contrapuntal at this point, inasmuch as we have two quite different structures fitting together in harmony. Many examples of this sort are known: one crystal growing on another, in precise mutual orientation, just because the atomic patterns fit along one plane of each crystal. Mineral crystals are sometimes found in association in this way, and many more examples have been discovered by experiments. One of the best known is the parallel growth of sodium nitrate on a cleavage rhomb of calcite (also shown in Fig. 58); the atoms in sodium nitrate are arranged in the same way as in calcite, with much the same distances, and this substance crystallizes in the form of simple rhombohedra. Calcite crystals found in nature are usually not rhombohedra, but can be cleaved easily into rhombohedral pieces; if a drop of warm strong solution of sodium nitrate is put on a cleavage surface of calcite covered with a glass plate and allowed to cool, little crystals grow, mostly

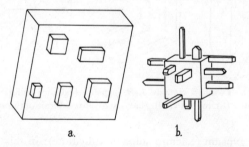

a.   b.

FIG. 58.   Oriented overgrowths. (a) Sodium nitrate on calcite. (b) Urea on ammonium chloride.

in perfectly parallel alignment. In this case the atomic arrangements in the two substances correspond completely in all directions, but complete correspondence is not necessary; a good fit on one plane of each substance is sufficient, as we have already seen in the example of urea on ammonium chloride. Another good example is the growth of ammonium iodide crystals on a cleavage surface of one type of mica (phlogopite); the ammonium iodide forms triangular crystals growing, precisely oriented, on the mica (see Plate 7) because the atomic patterns fit; but some of them are upside down with respect to the others, because the triangular pattern of ammonium iodide fits on the mica equally well either way up. In other respects the atomic patterns are quite different. On another type of mica (lepidolite) the ammonium iodide triangles are all the same way up on an atomically perfect cleavage surface, and the opposite way up if the cleavage happens to occur at another level of the mica structure (as shown in Plate 7b there is evidently an invisible step from one level to another).

Sometimes two crystals of the same species are found fitting together on one particular plane, in the Siamese twin fashion illustrated in Fig. 59, which shows, on the left, a "butterfly

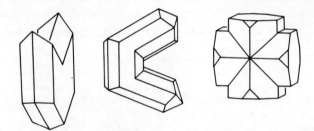

Fig. 59.   Twinned crystals. *Left:* gypsum (calcium sulfate hydrate). *Center:* rutile (titanium oxide). *Right:* staurolite (aluminum iron silicate).

twin" of gypsum (calcium sulphate dihydrate); in this example of twinning, the lattice structures of the two crystals are differently oriented but fit (and of course fit perfectly) on one plane only, and one crystal is like the mirror image of the other. The junction plane is a common plane of atoms which belongs to both crystals. Gypsum is a crystal of low symmetry, but the composite twin attains a higher shape symmetry. This sort of thing is sometimes repeated, giving all sorts of composite forms. The second picture of Fig. 59 shows three crystals of rutile, a form of titanium oxide, joined in this way. The third is a remarkable example in which four individuals are joined to form a cross-shaped structure. This is another example in which twinning gives a structure having a higher shape symmetry than a single crystal.

In the examples so far given, the external shape betrays the twinned nature of the structure; nobody would mistake a butterfly twin of gypsum or a cross-shaped twin of staurolite for a single crystal, because the re-entrant angles give the game away. In some species, however, twinning can produce crystals which look like single crystals of a different symmetry. The ammonium sulfate crystal shown in the center of Fig. 60, for

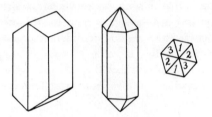

FIG. 60. Single crystals of ammonium sulfate have the shape on the left and are orthorhombic. A mimetic twin, of hexagonal shape, is shown in the center; it consists of six individuals with three different orientations as in the section on the right.

instance, looks like a hexagonal crystal; but most crystals of this substance are of a different shape (left, Fig. 60) and are undoubtedly orthorhombic. The hexagonal crystal is in fact a composite structure; this can be proved by measuring its optical properties and in other ways. What has happened is that six individuals are associated together in the way shown in the section; there are only three different orientations but six individuals. To make deception complete, the ends of the crystal are finished off with hexagonal pyramids. This sort of thing, which is often found, is called mimetic twinning. It reminds one of mimicry in the animal world, but of course has a much simpler origin.

An increase in symmetry is by no means always the outcome of twinning; look for instance at Fig. 61 which shows one of the most remarkable examples of twinning, sometimes found in crystals of fluorspar (calcium fluoride). Two cubes are joined in a most unexpected manner, giving a composite shape that has a lower symmetry than a cube. The relation between the two cubes can be described in the following way: if we start with one cube and rotate it around its body diagonal through 60°, we get to the position of the other cube. It looks as if the two cubes interpenetrate right through each other; there cannot of course be two complete crystal structures of different orientation occupying the same space, and what we should find if we could see the atoms is that in some places the lattice structure is right for one cube and in others it is right for the other cube. The boundary between the regions of different orientation in such composite twins as this is sometimes rather irregular—which makes it rather surprising that the external shape is so regular.

Our final variation in this series of crystal oddities is in a sense

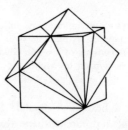

FIG. 61.   An "interpenetrating" twin of fluorspar (calcium fluoride).

the most extreme, for it can lead to the greatest departure from the straight-line schemes which are the ideals of the crystal kingdom. Some substances, under certain conditions, crystallize not as single crystals or twinned composite growths, but in the form of radial aggregates of needlelike crystals, looking like a hedgehog or a sea urchin. There is nothing surprising in that, if the structure originates in many different nuclei all formed together, each of which grows outward in needle form. But some radial growths are completely filled in to make a spherical shape, so that evidence of the radial character is only obtained by breaking open the sphere; moreover, in some of them it can be seen that, right at the center, there is a sheaflike structure (Fig. 62), suggesting that the whole spherical structure (or spherulite, as it is called) originated in a single crystal nucleus which soon splayed out at the ends to form a sheaf; subsequent growth of the splayed-out ends, with further distortion and filling in, led to the complete spherulite. We can hardly call a spherulite a single crystal, because on the outside it consists of many crystals in all possible orientations; but it appears to have grown from a single crystal by progressive distortion.

Spherulites of this type are formed from viscous liquids or jellies, and the extreme and progressive distortion may be attributed to interaction between the growing crystal and the viscous liquid or jelly. The substances used as plastics, when they crystallize (as some of them like polythene and nylon do), form these spherulitic structures (see Plate 8); the viscous liquids are somewhat rubbery and elastic, and we can imagine that the elastic liquid pulls the crystals out of shape; at any rate, the

FIG. 62. A complete spherulite originating in one crystal, which first splays out to become sheaflike and ultimately becomes completely radial.

crystals are certainly growing under difficulties, so that their deviation from the straight-line ideal is excusable. The distortion in spherulites reminds us of the distortion of ice crystals growing on window panes, which results in curved and sometimes branching growths; but here it is due to surface forces on the glass, whereas in the plastics it is the viscous and elastic nature of the crystallizing liquid that is responsible.

Is it surprising that polythene and nylon and other substances used as plastics manage to crystallize? In a way it is, because these substances consist of extremely long chain molecules, which in the melted liquid must be hopelessly tangled together. To form crystals the molecules have somehow to straighten themselves out and pack together in an orderly fashion, following what is in intention a straight-line packing scheme. They do not necessarily do this completely, but parts of the chains do manage to do it, forming very small crystalline regions. You cannot see crystal shapes inside plastic specimens, because for one thing the crystalline regions are much too small, and for another, the distortion leads to the spherulitic type of crystal growth. Normally you cannot even see spherulites in plastic specimens, again because they are too small, and special optical methods are necessary to reveal them; but the opacity of polythene and such substances is due to the scattering of light by the tiny spherulites. The crystallization in spherulites is the reason why they are opaque, in contrast to other plastics like "Perspex" which are clear and transparent because they do not crystallize. The photograph of polythene under the microscope, shown in Plate 8, was obtained by special optical methods; the strange effects of crystals on light are the subject of a later chapter.

For the finale of this chapter, let us return to the principal theme—the single crystal, perfect in form and structure (or as perfect as may be in this world where nothing is absolute), with no holes or flaws in its interior and with mirrorlike faces. The variations have taken us far from this ideal, and it is appropriate that we return to it before embarking on the next subject.

The near-perfect crystal, apart from being the crystallographer's ideal, is required by many scientists in their investigations, and is also highly desirable for many technological applications. The difficulty of obtaining sufficiently good specimens varies enormously from one species to another; every species has its own idiosyncracies, which have to be learnt by patient experiment. It also depends on the size required; the larger the crystal, the more difficult it is to preserve a sufficient approach to perfection. Quite large crystals are required for some purposes: for optical apparatus for the infrared range of light wavelengths, it is necessary to have lenses and prisms made of something other than glass, and certain crystals like fluorite and sodium chloride happen to be suitable, so crystals several inches across are grown for the purpose. Even when the size required is more modest, it is sometimes found convenient to grow large crystals and to cut them up into pieces of the right size. This is so for certain electrical applications; small plates are required, accurately cut in particular directions, for converting mechanical into electrical vibrations or for controlling the frequency of electrical oscillators, and for this purpose quite large crystals are grown, to provide a stock of near-perfect material for cutting up. These requirements have led to the development of methods for growing large crystals without internal flaws.

The electrical applications depend on an interesting phenomenon known as piezoelectricity: crystals having certain symmetries (quartz is one), if compressed in particular directions, develop a voltage between opposite surfaces, and conversely if a voltage is applied the crystal changes its dimensions slightly. It works either way, and we can either change an alternating pressure into an alternating voltage as in a phonograph pickup, or change an alternating voltage into an alternating pressure as in a generator of ultrasonic sound waves. Moreover, there is a resonant frequency depending on the thickness of the crystal plate, and this is utilized in the extremely accurate control of electrical frequencies in radio transmitters and electric clocks. Natural quartz crystals are used for these purposes, but other crystals, grown artificially, have been introduced in recent years.

The secret of growing large flawless crystals is usually to grow them very slowly and steadily. For a substance that is very soluble in water, the usual method is to prepare small seed crystals to start with, and put them in a saturated solution that is cooled very slowly. The temperature is controlled by a thermostat whose regulating temperature is adjusted downward by, say, one-tenth of a degree per day. The seeds are mounted on stems and moved about to keep the solution stirred; any new nuclei formed in the solution are not wanted, and are redissolved, for instance by having a small local source of heat at the bottom of the vessel where they fall. Rochelle salt (sodium potassium tartrate) and ammonium dihydrogen phosphate are piezoelectric crystals that are grown in this way. Some crystals are best grown from molten material; one method is to have a seed crystal (on a stem holder) just touching the surface of the melt, and to cool the seed from above through its stem; the seed grows, and is gradually raised as it grows. Another method is to cool the melt from below, very slowly, until the whole of it has crystallized; with luck, the whole of the melt becomes one single crystal, or at any rate a very small number of individuals.

Crystals of germanium and silicon for transistors are required to have an extraordinarily high standard of purity, and this is attained by a special form of crystallizing procedure called zone melting. The material is contained in a long tube, and an electric heater surrounding the tube is moved very slowly along it (see Fig. 63). This achieves two goals simultaneously. The

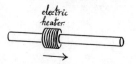

FIG. 63. The zone melting process for growing very pure crystals. The material is contained in the tube, and the heater is moved very slowly along the tube.

material is melted, and when it cools, crystallizes again; and as the temperature change is very slow, it forms a single crystal which gradually grows along the tube. In addition to this, impurities are rejected; a growing crystal face traps impurities if growth is fast but rejects them if it is slow. The result of the very slow movement of the melted zone is that the impurities are gradually moved along to one end of the tube, leaving the germanium or silicon crystals much purer. By repeating the process, it is possible to attain the very high standard of purity necessary in transistor crystals.

CHAPTER 8

Jewels

Colored stones and transparent crystals have excited admiration and curiosity since the beginnings of civilization and (one can guess) long before; their beauty and desirability, and the rarity of good specimens, naturally led to their being prized as personal ornaments, and the striking effects of light and color gave rise to many superstitions about them. To what extent the mystery of their natural shapes played a part in the fascination the early civilized people felt for them is problematical, but in the Greco-Roman civilization in the Mediterranean 2000 years ago it is surprising to find that gem stones were not "cut" into the shapes with flat facets that are familiar nowadays. Those for ornamental purposes were polished to rounded shapes, while others intended for use as seals or just kept as miniature works of art had symbols or pictures engraved in low relief on them. (The art of gem engraving was technically close to, and may have been suggested by, that of making coin dies.) The shapes of natural crystals are seldom good enough to make them acceptable as they are for ornamental purposes. Some of those attached to rock masses can be removed without spoiling them except at the attachment end, but the shapes are all too often not sufficiently regular. Detached crystals are often found in river beds, washed down with other rock debris, but these are usually rounded by attrition, so that little or no trace of the original shape remains. Thus in either case something must be done to improve their appearance. The rounded crystals found in river beds doubtless suggested the simplest way of fashioning ornaments: all that was necessary was to grind the surface to whatever curvature was fancied (and which did not waste too much of the original material), and to polish it to give full play to the light-reflecting powers of the stone and to bring out the color. The origin of the custom of fashioning rounded polished stones thus seems natural enough; still, it remains surprising that the natural shapes of crystals found in rock fissures did not suggest in a similar way the possibility of grinding and polishing flat surfaces—especially to the Greeks, who were highly conscious of the beauty and mystical significance of geometrical figures. It rather looks as if the Greeks did not think very much about the natural geometrical shapes of crystals, otherwise they would not have ignored this feature in their treatment of precious stones. For all their love of geometry, for some reason they did not respect the natural geometry displayed by minerals. This is to me one of the curiosities of history.

The qualities a natural stone must have if it is to be treasured for its own sake or used for personal adornment are, of course, first of all, the ability to reflect light well, and secondly, the ability to give pleasing or striking color effects. The ability to reflect light well depends first of all on the smoothness of the surface, but it also depends on an intrinsic property of the material called the refractive index; the higher the refractive index, the brighter the reflections from a smooth surface. This same property, the refractive index, controls the amount of bending a ray of light undergoes when it passes from the air into the solid; it is, in fact, a fundamental property of the material depending on the nature of the atoms composing it. Color effects may be due either to the intrinsic color of the stone, as in rubies and emeralds, or to the flashing effects called "fire" which are produced pre-eminently by colorless stones like diamond. We shall return to these color effects later; meanwhile, a third quality that is very desirable is hardness. Unless a stone is harder than any object it is likely to come in contact with, and harder than the dust particles that are certain to rub on it, it will inevitably become scratched. Consequently, only the hardest materials make successful durable jewels. Hardness is a quality that is not easy to measure in a quantitative scientific way, but it *is* possible to arrange solid substances in order of hardness, by finding out which scratches which. Quartz scratches calcite (marble), and is therefore said to be harder than calcite. Corundum (alumina, rubies, and sapphires) scratches quartz, and diamond, which scratches everything else, is the hardest substance known. The conventional hardness scale gives diamond the number 10, corundum 9, topaz 8, quartz 7, felspar 6, apatite 5, fluorite 4, calcite 3, gypsum 2, and talc 1; the numbers have no quantitative significance—they only give the order of hardness. Since dust, almost anywhere, is likely to contain particles of sand (quartz) or other soil minerals having a similar hardness, it follows that only substances that are harder than quartz are really durable jewels; and since quartz is quite high up in the hardness scale, the number of first-rate gem minerals is small. The less hard stones like marcasite are, of course, used in less expensive jewelry; they are beautiful but not scratchproof; they are much less durable than rubies and diamonds.

The hardest stones are naturally the most difficult to shape and polish, for any stone can only be worked by substances at least as hard as itself; the difficulty of working, added to the rarity, explains the high prices of good jewels. The hardness, added to their beauty, also contributes to their reputation as the aristocracy of the mineral kingdom.

Hardness is a matter of the strength of the forces holding the atoms of a crystal together; the hardest crystals are those in which the forces between the atoms are very strong, and these crystals are also the ones that are very stable with respect to heat and can only be melted at very high temperatures. They are the crystals that were formed by solidification of molten material early in the world's history—the material now known as the "igneous" rocks. ("Igneous" means "produced by the action of fire.") Many igneous rocks like granite contain small crystals of some of the species used as jewels (beryl, topaz, zircon, corundum, garnet, spinel, tourmaline, and others)— you can see them glinting on the surfaces—but they are not large enough. Bigger crystals are found in what the geologist calls pegmatite dikes and veins, which probably crystallized later than the finer-grained rocks nearby: first of all, volcanic lava, collecting in cracks and hollows in the earth's crust, slowly crystallized; when much of it had crystallized in a fine-grained form, the remaining mother liquor, which by this time contained a certain amount of water under pressure, was squeezed out along crevices, where it formed a more coarsely crystalline rock. But gem stones are usually not taken directly from such rocks; they are found as pebbles in river beds or other alluvial deposits where they have been washed down by water along with other fragments of weathered disintegrated rocks; it is sometimes possible to trace the pebbles upstream and so to locate the original source. Near the source the crystals may be fairly sharp and clear, but lower down they may be so rounded and roughened that they look much the same as ordinary pebbles: an expert eye is required to spot them.

Diamonds stand apart from other gems, in this as in many other ways. There is no mystery about the origin of most gems: they obviously crystallized directly from molten rock material of appropriate composition, and they can be made in the laboratory in a similar way. But the origin of diamonds is still a mystery. They are found in South Africa and in Siberia in a sort of marl known as "blue ground" contained in vertical volcanic pipes; but they may not have crystallized in this blue ground: some people believe they are of earlier origin. Diamond is a form of carbon. Small crystals have been made in the laboratory under very high pressure, and this may have been the way in which natural diamonds were formed; but there appears to be no definite evidence to indicate whether or not they were formed in this way. Small diamonds are sometimes found in meteorites, associated with iron, which in the liquid state does dissolve carbon; they may have actually crystallized out of a solution of carbon in molten iron.

A well-formed crystal with mirrorlike facets and free from internal flaws is a beautiful object, worth preserving just as it is, for the permanent admiration and delight of its owner and anyone else who happens to see it. Such crystals are often found in cavities in rocks, growing on some underlying rock material which, when detached, may serve as a natural setting. The best specimens have found their way into museums, but many amateur collectors are proud to possess specimens which are their equals in quality, if not in size. Groups of crystals found in such situations (see Plate 1) are often particularly attractive: the arrangement sometimes has a natural balance which, if it were the work of a man, would evoke comments on the artist's sense of form—a natural balance reminiscent of trees and flowers, giving a satisfying sense of unity as well as the interest and pleasure of diversity of detail. This unity and balance has its origin, of course, in the processes of crystal growth—the laying down of the crystal nuclei in certain places, and then the growth of them, the sharing out of the available material by the interplay of the natural growth characteristics of the crystals themselves with the influence of the surroundings. Our sense of unity and balance, whether in a shrub or a nest of crystals, is, I think, due to our instinctive subconscious appreciation of such processes. just as our appreciation of music has in it subconscious mathematics.

Naturalists, whether or not they call themselves crystallographers, will prefer their crystal specimens preserved as nearly as possible in the state in which they were found. But for personal adornment or for incorporation in the Crown Jewels, crystals must be shaped and polished. The natural shape of a crystal may not be suitable for the purpose in mind, and the faces may not be the ones best suited for bringing out the play of light; worse still, there may be internal flaws which prevent the crystal from coming up to the standard of dazzling perfection aimed at by jewelers. For internal flaws there is no cure, and if perfect transparency is considered essential, there is no alternative to the course of breaking or cutting the crystal into such pieces as are perfect; the pieces must then be shaped, polished and mounted.

There are two ways of breaking down a crystal into smaller pieces: one is to make use of its natural cleavages, if it has any; the other is to saw it through. Many crystals break most readily along certain planes where the cohesive forces are weaker than in other directions, and if these planes are convenient for the desired breakdown, a good deal of time and trouble can be saved by making use of them. It may seem a risky method to use with such precious material, but experienced workers use it with little risk of failure; a notch is scratched with a diamond

point, and then a blunt knife, with its edge in the notch and
its plane parallel to the cleavage plane of the crystal, is struck
sharply; whereupon the crystal falls neatly into two pieces with
flat (often mirrorlike) surfaces. This method is much used for
diamonds, because the octahedral cleavage gives a good start in
the making of the shape known as a "brilliant," which has been
found to be particularly good for displaying the flashing "fire"
which is the glory of diamonds. The other method is to saw
the crystal into pieces. This is done by a revolving phosphor-
bronze disk wheel one-tenth of a millimeter thick, the edge of
which is charged with diamond dust hammered into the metal.
It is essential that the abrasive material should be as hard as,
or harder than, the crystal being sawn, and since diamond is the
hardest natural crystal, it will do for all gems.

When the stone has been cut roughly to the desired shape in
this way, faces are then made by grinding first the larger facets
and then the smaller ones: the stone, cemented to a stick so that
it can be held conveniently, is held against a rapidly revolving
cast-iron wheel on which is a mixture of abrasive and either
oil or water. The angles are set by resting the stick in notches
in an attachment to the bench. The abrasive depends on the
hardness of the stone; diamond dust is the only thing to use
for diamonds, but for other stones carborundum or emery may
be suitable. Naturally for the final polishing the finest abrasive
powder is used.

Cutting diamonds is much, much more difficult and tedious
than cutting any other stones; diamond is far harder than any
other known substance, and therefore the only way of dealing
with it is to rub it against itself—a process necessarily much
slower than for other gems, for which an abrasive harder than
the stone can be used. The tediousness of the process may be
gathered from the fact that the initial sawing, for any but the
smallest stones, takes many hours or even several days. It is not
surprising, then, that diamond cutters are a class apart; they
insist on being called diamond cutters and nothing else, as
opposed to those who work with other stones, who are called
gem cutters or lapidaries. After the initial sawing, which gives

the basic overall shape to the stone, comes the grinding of the little facets which do so much to enhance the decorative appearance. This is done by diamond dust and is again very tedious; and it is not simply a matter of deciding how the facet shall be placed, and grinding in any direction until enough material has been removed, for it has been found that grinding in certain directions is much more effective than in other directions on the same surface: it is necessary to take account of the "grain" of the crystal structure, in this as in many other ways.

The artificial faces which are created in this manner do not, in general, correspond to natural faces of the crystal, or even to planes related in a simple way to the internal structure though not appearing as natural faces. The larger ones may (particularly if cleavages were used in the initial shaping), but the smaller ones are chosen without regard to the internal structure. They are chosen to give a pleasing appearance to the stone in its final setting, and to give the most brilliant effects of light and color. To the purist crystallographer this may seem sacrilege—rather like clipping shrubs to the shapes of peacocks or sailing ships —inappropriate, and showing deplorable taste. But it has to be admitted that, in compensation for the violation of the natural form, there is often a great gain in pleasing appearance, and, above all, in the brilliance of the light effects: what we lose in morphology we gain in optics, for the shapes chosen for jewels are designed to send back to the observer as much as possible of the light which falls on the stone—not only the light reflected externally by the facets, but also some of the light which enters the crystal, which by successive internal reflections comes back again to the eye. It is this internally reflected light which is responsible for some of the most beautiful light effects given by jewels—the flashes of mysterious colored light called "fire," which are given by many stones that are in themselves colorless. This is one of the qualities for which diamond is prized, and is due to the fact that the various colored rays of which white light is composed are bent and reflected differently inside the crystal, so that they are sent in different directions and strike the eye separately as the stone is moved.

One of the shapes which is much favored for producing these beautiful light effects, and is widely used for diamonds, is known as the "brilliant cut," illustrated in Fig. 64, which also tries to show how the light effects are produced. When light goes from air into a transparent solid with a flat surface, its direction is bent, to a degree expressed by a figure called the "refractive index"; the higher the refractive index, the greater the bending. But the refractive index is not the same for all colors of light— it is greater for light at the violet end of the spectrum than at the red end—consequently the light is spread out into a spectrum inside the crystal. When it gets to another face of the crystal, its behavior depends on the angle at which it strikes the face; if it strikes it nearly at right angles, it will pass out of the crystal more or less in the same direction—and for a jewel set in a ring, this means it will be absorbed in the mounting material. But if the angle deviates from a right angle by more than a certain

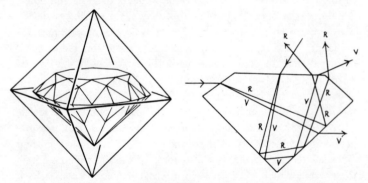

Fig. 64. *Left:* The "brilliant" cut, shown in relation to the octahedral shape of a natural diamond crystal. *Right:* Light rays in a diamond "brilliant"; they are reflected at the back surfaces and emerge at the front, separated into colors (R — red, V — violet). The "fire" of diamonds is due to this combination of refraction and internal reflection.

"critical angle," it does not get out at all, but is totally reflected internally, and, as the diagram shows, this means that it finds its way out of the top of the crystal after one or two internal reflections. By this time the colors are well separated so that the eye sees one at a time as the stone is moved about. These colors are of course similar to those given by the glass prism ornaments which were much favored in Victorian times; the difference is that light goes right through the glass prisms, whereas in jewels the light is sent back by successive reflections inside the crystals. The critical angle depends on the refractive index; the higher the refractive index, the smaller the critical angle, and the more chance there is for total internal reflection. This is why diamond is better than most other crystals—it has an extremely high refractive index, 2.4, and a low critical angle, $24\frac{1}{2}°$ for yellow light; these figures should be compared with 1.76 and 35° for corundum (of which rubies and sapphires are colored varieties) and 1.52 and $40\frac{1}{2}°$ for ordinary crown glass. There is also a further effect which helps to separate the colors when the light is going in an appropriate direction: the critical angle is not the same for different colors of light, and, moreover, since the different colors are going in somewhat different directions, it sometimes happens that red light and yellow light are reflected (the angle being greater than the critical angle) while blue and violet pass through (because the angle is less than the critical angle) and are absorbed by the mounting material; only the red and yellow therefore return to the eye. This is no doubt the origin of the term "fire" used in describing the flashing of diamonds. These effects are very striking in diamond, because both its refractive index and its "dispersion" (the difference between the refractive indices for red and violet light) are high, but it is not pre-eminent in this; the gem known as "sphene" (mineral name titanite, a calcium titanium silicate) gives even more brilliant fire owing to its higher dispersion—it gives flashes of unusually intense red and blue. Unfortunately, it is too soft to be used for brooches and rings.

Rubies and sapphires are often made into "brilliants" (Fig. 65). But the "step cut" is often used for colored stones, especially flat ones: it retains the greatest area for the display of the color, and the beveling facets help to give a pleasing appearance. It is less suited to display "fire" by internal reflection, but this effect is of less importance for stones which are intrinsically colored.

The wonderful colors of some types of gem stones are pro-
verbial—the beautiful sky blue of sapphires, the thrilling deep
red of rubies, and the rich green of emeralds. What is not so
generally realized is that the colors of most gems are not the
natural colors of the pure crystals, but are due to very small
quantities of other substances (impurities, if you like) incorporated
in the crystals during their growth millions of years ago. Rubies
and sapphires are both varieties of crystalline aluminum oxide,
corundum, which in the pure state is quite colorless; the red
color of rubies is due to the presence of small quantities of
chromium, while the blue of sapphires is due to traces of iron
and titanium. The physicochemical processes responsible for
these colors are still not understood; minute quantities of various

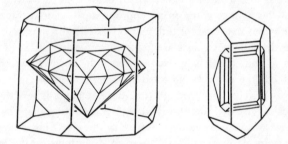

FIG. 65. Jewel shapes and their relation to the original crystals.
Left: ruby; *right:* tourmaline (the "step cut").

impurities can be detected by chemical or spectroscopic analysis,
but it is not always known which is responsible for the color.
Our knowledge of these matters has been extended in recent
years by the experience gained in making gem stones synthe-
tically, as we shall see later in this chapter.

Emerald is quite a different species from rubies and sapphires
—it is beryllium aluminum silicate, the mineral beryl (Fig. 66);
but again the wonderful rich green color of many emeralds is
not the natural color of the basic substance: pure beryl is colorless, the green color of emeralds being due to the presence of a
minute amount of chromium. Beryl is also found in blue, sea

green, pink, rose, and golden yellow varieties—but the blue and sea green varieties are known as aquamarines.

The color effects of gem stones are almost endless. One of the most variable of all is tourmaline, which basically is an alumino-silicate of very complex composition; it may be colorless, red in many shades, yellow, green, blue, or black. Some crystals have quite different colors at the two ends—for example, green at one end and red at the other—or there may be bands of various colors along a prism-shaped crystal. Stones with a green rind and a pink interior are known. All these effects are due to the presence of different "impurities" in different parts of the same crystal (because, presumably, the liquid which fed the crystal

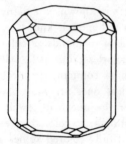

Fig. 66.   The shape of a natural emerald (the mineral name is beryl).

carried at different times small amounts of different substances). To complete the tale of versatility, crystals of tourmaline often appear to be different in color if one looks through them in different directions; one crystal will be yellow if light comes through in one direction, green in another; other crystals are brown and red for the two directions, or lavender and rose. This effect is due to the remarkable phenomenon known as pleochroism, which is explained later in this book—a phenomenon strange in its effects, and deeply significant for our understanding of the nature of light as well as of the structure of crystals.

The colors of natural stones can sometimes be altered by suitable heat treatment. One of the largest precious stones ever found was a yellowish-green aquamarine weighing 220 pounds;

it was found in Brazil in 1910; cut in Germany, it yielded 200,000 carats (90 pounds weight) of gem stones. The original color was not especially good, but it was found that by cautious heating it could be changed to a rich sea blue. It is now customary to heat green aquamarines to turn them blue. Similarly, yellow topaz crystals can be changed to a rose color by careful heating. Zircons are sometimes found in dark red, brown, or yellow forms, and some of these can be turned blue by heating; but not all—some are rendered colorless (the natural state of pure zirconium silicate). The chemical changes are unknown.

Quartz, one of the forms of silica, is another mineral which in the pure state is colorless, but it is often found in colored varieties, which are more prized than the colorless pure substance. Mauve quartz is known as amethyst, yellow as citrine; a green variety with red spots is known as bloodstone.

Most people think of diamonds as colorless—and indeed the pure substance *is* colorless; but pale yellow or smoky brown diamonds are far more common than colorless ones. Not unnaturally, the colorless ones are most favored generally—it is felt perhaps that for the queen of jewels color is unnecessary (moreover, the commonest colored ones are not especially attractive); but beautifully colored stones are sometimes found, and command high prices. The colors are not very deep—golden yellow, orange, rose, lavender pink, aquamarine, pale sapphire blue, and green—but a few rare and famous ones are quite deeply colored: the Dresden diamond is a rich green, the Tiffany diamond a rich orange yellow; and a beautiful deep pink diamond was presented to Queen Elizabeth II (then Princess Elizabeth). A deep blue diamond was brought back from India in 1638 by Tavernier, a French geographer, and sold to Louis XIV in 1668, when it became part of the French crown jewels. It was stolen during the revolution in 1792, but reappeared later, much reduced in size, as the Hope diamond (named after the London dealer who secured it); it is now owned by a New York dealer.

There are a few exceptions to the general rule that the colors of most gem stones are due to accidental traces of impurities. The blue of turquoise is intrinsic—it is a hydrated copper aluminum phosphate, and copper compounds are often blue; and the deep blue of lapis lazuli (a sodium aluminosilicate sulfide) is also an invariable characteristic of its structure. Dioptase, a copper silicate, is always rich green, owing to the copper which is an essential structural constituent of the crystal; urovarite, a chrome garnet, is always green, and hematite (iron oxide) always red.

The appearance of some crystals is enhanced by internal markings due to inclusions arranged in a regular pattern. "Star sapphires" show, as the name implies, internal star-shaped markings, due to the presence of minute inclusions arranged in a hexagonal manner; sapphire, it will be remembered, is a blue variety of corundum which is a crystal of hexagonal symmetry —hence the hexagonal arrangement of the inclusions. Another fascinating effect is that shown by "cat's eye," which is trans-lucent chrysoberyl (beryllium aluminate) of honey to greenish-yellow color crowded with minute inclusions; a stone cut "en cabochon"—i.e., as a rounded cushion—shows a white line of silky sheen which seems to move across the surface as the stone is tilted. Still another phenomenon is the occurrence of "ghosts" inside crystals—shadowy outlines repeating the external shape on a smaller scale in the interior. This sort of thing, which occurs particularly in quartz, is really very simple in origin: particles of some impurity are at one stage deposited on the crystal faces, and then become sealed in as the crystal continues to grow; but before the origin and growth of crystals was under-stood, such "ghosts" must have seemed very mysterious.

Most jewels are of course quite small, not more than a few carats in weight (a carat is the one hundred and fortieth part of an ounce). Natural crystals perfect enough for jewels are rare, because to be perfect a crystal must grow slowly and very steadily, and the right conditions were probably not often realized in nature. Moreover, the larger a crystal becomes, the more steadily it must be grown if perfection is to be maintained, so, on the whole, the larger a crystal is, the more likely it is to have blemishes. The really large crystals of the finest species are justly famous, and often go by historic names. One of them, the Hope diamond, has been mentioned. Another historic diamond, the Koh-i-noor, was discovered, so the legend runs, 5000 years ago in the Godavari River in India; but the first authentic record of it bears the date 1526, when it was in the possession of Sultan Baber. Its name, given to it by Nadir in 1739, means "mountain of light." Later it passed to the East India Company with the stipulation that it be presented to the Queen of England. It is now among the British Crown Jewels. But the Koh-i-noor is not the largest diamond ever found; this distinction belongs to the Cullinan, found in South Africa in 1905; it weighed 3106 carats (about a pound and a half) before being cut.

Really large emeralds, rubies, and sapphires likewise go by famous names. The "Star of India" is a star sapphire weighing 563 carats. There is a sapphire of 260 carats in the Russian state collection. A ruby of 100 carats known as the De Longstar ruby is now in the American Museum of Natural History. One of the largest emeralds known is a rich green one found in Colombia; it was originally a hexagonal crystal, but was made into an unguent jar weighing 2680 carats (nearly $1\frac{1}{2}$ pounds) by Miseroni, a Milanese gem engraver; it is now in the Vienna state collection. Of all the precious stones, aquamarines (blue or sea green forms of beryl) are found in the largest good-quality crystals; the enormous one of 220 pounds found in Brazil has already been mentioned.

In earlier days, precious stones were naturally classified largely by color; any deep red stone was called a ruby, and blue stones were usually called sapphires. We know now that color is not an essential characteristic of some of the finest species, it is an accidental feature due to small traces of impurities; and that several species can be deep red, and the same several species can be blue. It is therefore not surprising that many a jewel (including some very famous ones) formerly thought to be one species has been shown to be in fact another. Not that it matters much to those to whom jewels are primarily things of beauty or rare ornaments: a rose by any other name would smell as sweet, and a ruby by any other name would look just as magnificent. But naturalists are justifiably fussy about these things, and to them it is a matter of absorbing interest to know just what crystal species a famous jewel really is. One of the outstanding examples of mistaken identity is the "Black Prince Ruby" now in front of the British crown; this historic stone was given to the Black Prince by Pedro the Cruel in 1367, and was later worn by Henry V on his helmet crown at the battle of Agincourt; but it is not a ruby (a red corundum) at all, but a red spinel. These two species are quite different in chemical composition and structure; corundum is aluminum oxide, with two aluminum atoms to every three oxygens (Al_2O_3), and its crystals have hexagonal symmetry and grow in the shape shown in Fig. 67a; but spinel is magnesium aluminate, with one magnesium to every two aluminum and four oxygen atoms ($MgAl_2O_4$), and its crystals are cubic in symmetry and grow as shown in Fig. 67b.

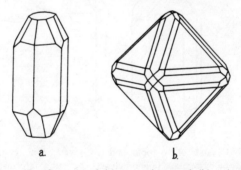

a.   b.

FIG. 67.   Crystals of (a) corundum and (b) spinel.

Then there is a "ruby" which was given to Catherine the Great of Russia by Gustavus III of Sweden; but it turned out to be rubellite, a red variety of tourmaline. This crystal species is so complex chemically, and so variable, that it would serve little purpose to quote a formula; it grows in longish prisms of trigonal symmetry, and, as I have already mentioned, is extremely variable in color as well as composition.

The practice of using incorrect names for precious stones still continues to this day, but no longer through ignorance but more

as a matter of fashion, and the commercial reasons depending
on fashion. A particular color is associated with a particular
mineral name, and any stone having that color is likely to be
called by the commonly associated name. Topaz, for instance,
is very often yellow—not invariably so, for it can be colorless or
even blue—but most people tend to think of topaz as a yellow
stone, consequently any good yellow stone is liable to be called
a topaz. Actually the mineral commonly offered as topaz is
really a yellow variety of quartz, and ought to be called citrine.
The two are completely different crystal species. Topaz is an
aluminum fluosilicate of orthorhombic symmetry which grows
as crystals shaped like in Fig. 68a; quartz we have met before

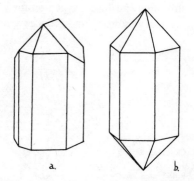

a.   b.

Fig. 68. Crystals of (a) topaz and (b) quartz. The crystal of topaz
is broken at the basal plane (a good cleavage); doubly terminated crystals
are rare.

several times in this book—it has one atom of silicon to every
two of oxygen, arranged in a rather complex hexagonal structure
which grows in the prismatic form illustrated in Fig. 68b.
Incidentally quartz, which in the pure state is colorless, occurs
also in mauve forms called amethyst; and as the word amethyst
has become firmly attached to mauve stones, and quartz is the
commonest mauve colored mineral, stones bought as "amethysts"
probably are genuine mauve quartz crystals.

Precious stones have been credited with powers of healing or of magic, either beneficial or malevolent, throughout the period for which there is any recorded evidence. Some of these beliefs were due to simple and obvious, though superficial and fallacious, associations of ideas; rubies have sometimes been supposed to have the power of stopping the flow of blood, yellow stones to cure jaundice, and amethysts to cure drunkenness. Others seem to have been due to a vague general idea that gems have magical powers: the wearing of gems as talismans protecting the wearer against harm has been common through the ages, and still goes on today, though belief in their virtue is much diluted. Amulets were often made up of several different precious stones, to combine the protective powers of all of them, and give the wearer the comforting feeling of having taken out a comprehensive insurance policy.

In the early civilizations in Egypt and Mesopotamia, precious stones, engraved with suitable inscriptions or designs, were fashioned into shapes suitable for use as seals for impressing the designs on softer materials. Babylonian seals were usually in cylindrical form so that they could be rolled on the sealing wax, but Egyptian seals often had the shape of a scarab, a particular kind of beetle which had a symbolic significance. The symbolism arose from a curious train of associated ideas: in the first place, since only fully grown beetles were observed (the connection with the earlier metamorphic forms of the insect being unsuspected), they were thought to be reincarnations, and thus symbolized immortality; moreover, the beetle is a ball-rolling species, and on this account was regarded as a symbol of the world (for the Egyptians did realize that the earth is a ball). Scarabs were therefore not merely seals but also had a magical significance and were often worn as talismans. Later on, in the Roman Imperial era, astrological symbols were engraved on gems, and still later, in the early Christian period, complex Gnostic symbols are found. The use of precious stones for such purposes was, no doubt, partly due to their hardness, permanence, and beauty of appearance, but also owed something to the feeling that the stones themselves had magical properties.

Not all the engraved gems of the ancient world, however, had official or superstitious designs on them: in the Greek and Roman civilizations especially, gem engraving became a much favored art form, and the permanence of the material has ensured that many exquisite examples of these miniature works of art (called cameos if the design is in relief, or intaglios if it is sunk in the stone) still exist in our museums and in private collections. The designs were often portraits or symbolic figures, fashioned for purely artistic reasons. In Roman times, collecting engraved gems became a rich man's hobby, and high prices were paid for particularly fine or rare specimens.

In medieval times the art of gem engraving seems to have been lost, and engraved gems, when found, were sometimes thought to be of natural origin and were regarded with superstitious awe owing to the designs on them. In somewhat the same way, crystals of chiastolite or macle which show crosses on their surfaces were thought to have magical properties, but these crosses really are natural, for this substance grows as finger-shaped crystals which, when broken, show crosses on the exposed new surfaces, the crosses being impurities incorporated along crystal axes during the growth of the crystals.

Some precious stones are phosphorescent: after exposure to strong light they will glow in the dark, some of the stored light energy being re-emitted; but the amount of light produced in this way is certainly not sufficient to justify the description of the throne of the Byzantine emperor Manuel (1120–1180) given by the Hebrew traveler Benjamin of Tudela: he mentions a throne of gold studded with precious stones, and above it, suspended from a canopy by golden chains, a magnificent golden crown set with jewels of incalculable value and so bright and sparkling that at night "no other form of illumination was necessary." Benjamin was evidently well entertained during his visit.

The realization that precious stones were formed naturally by the solidification of molten material of suitable composition has led in recent years to attempts to make them artificially; and indeed, nearly all the crystal species used as gems have been obtained by melting up the necessary ingredients and allowing the molten material to cool slowly. None of the crystals grown by this method, however, have been sufficiently large and perfect for use as jewels. For instance, two Frenchmen, Fremy and Hautefeuille, succeeded in growing rubies as long ago as 1877 by cooling a melt of alumina containing a little chromium oxide to give the red color; but the crystals which grew were very thin and platelike (the largest being only one-third of a carat in weight) and so were useless as gems. There is no reason to suppose that there is any mystery about the growth of larger crystals in nature, or that some unknown constituent is necessary in the melt to influence the manner of crystallization: the crystals found in the rocks probably grew exceedingly slowly by extremely slow cooling, under high pressures as well as high temperatures, and the conditions used in laboratory attempts to grow them have been *very* different. Everyone who has tried to grow good crystals knows that speed is all-important: the slower the better, and the hard intractable substances used as jewels need to be crystallized very much more slowly than soft materials like sugar or salt. Growth of precious stones by a method closely imitating the natural process would evidently have to be so slow that it would be quite uneconomic.

Success in growing gem stones sufficiently large and perfect to be used as jewels, and at a rate which made the process commercially feasible, eventually came in a most unexpected way. Another Frenchman, Verneuil, discovered in 1902 that by allowing finely powdered alumina (tapped gradually through a sieve to fall through a very hot (oxyhydrogen) flame so that each particle melted and then dropped onto the flat end of a corundum rod, he could grow quite large single crystals. The arrangement is shown in Fig. 69. It seems surprising that such a process, so completely different from that by which natural gems are formed, should be so successful, but there it is: crystal growing is an art, and a particularly difficult one for the hard, high-melting substances used as jewels, and the best methods have to be found by patient experiment. Probably the molten droplets of alumina are still molten when they first reach the solid surface of the rod, and when they solidify they carry on the structure already existing in the rod; no doubt a nice control of the temperature at the surface is necessary to keep the process going slowly and steadily. The rod is very slowly lowered by a screw motion, and as it moves downward the crystal broadens as it grows, so that it takes on an inverted pear shape known as a "boule."

A boule grown by the Verneuil method is quite literally a single crystal; it is not glassy, nor is it an aggregate of crystals; it is a single crystal which, if pure alumina is used, is colorless corundum, with the hexagonal axis of the internal structure along the axis of the rod which is the principal direction of growth. The sides of the boule are usually smooth and rounded, though occasionally a rough hexagonal outline can be seen; the top is

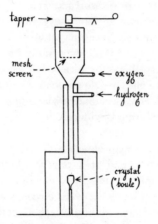

FIG. 69. The Verneuil apparatus for growing sapphires and rubies. See text for description of process.

on the whole rounded, but is not smooth—it is roughened by the presence of a finegrain staircase of facets. A boule can be grown at the rate of about 12 carats ($2\frac{1}{2}$ grams) an hour; the final size may be as much as 250 carats (50 grams, or just over 2 ounces). Rubies are made by adding $2\frac{1}{2}\%$ of chromium oxide to the alumina; the two substances are obtained as a very intimate mixture by coprecipitation from a mixed solution of aluminum and chromium salts. Magnesium has to be rigorously excluded, as it gives a brick-red instead of the deep rich blood-red color of the best natural stones. Sapphires are made by adding one-half per cent of titanium oxide and $1\frac{1}{2}\%$ of magnetic iron oxide to the alumina. A lavender color can be obtained by adding titanium oxide alone, and a rich yellow by adding nickel oxide. The stones are cut and shaped by the same methods as are used for the natural stones.

There is nothing "imitation" about these synthetic stones; they must not be confused with imitation jewels made from lead glass ("paste" is the word normally used to describe them), which have quite different properties, and resemble the natural stones only in transparency and color. The synthetic rubies and sapphires grown by the Verneuil process are the real thing —they have the same density, the same hardness, the same refractive index, and the same dichroism as the natural stones (for the meaning of "dichroism," see Chapter 10). They are of the finest gem quality—they have the same transparency and rich colors as the best natural stones: in short, they look as beautiful and they will wear just as well as natural stones, unlike "paste" imitations which are all too easily scratched and rubbed. They do in fact contain the same atoms arranged in the same way as in the natural stones. They differ from natural stones only in very slight secondary features due to the different manner of growth: under a microscope or a hand lens, both natural and synthetic stones show minute cavities (which in the natural stones are angular, but in the synthetic ones rounded) or streaks (which are straight in natural but curved in synthetic stones). In fact, if you buy rubies or sapphires, there is no point in insisting on natural stones, unless you want to get a romantic thrill from the thought that your jewels came from some distant part of the world where they crystallized millions of years ago. If you are concerned with beauty of appearance, or permanence, or with authenticity of crystal species, the synthetic stones are just as genuine as the natural ones.

Another crystal species which has been grown successfully by the Verneuil process is spinel, a crystal of cubic symmetry; good blue stones have been made from a mixture of cobalt,

magnesium and aluminum oxides. Beryls have been grown
successfully by a different process—evidently a hydrothermal
process, for the stones contain minute liquid enclosures with
bubbles in them; hexagonal prisms up to 2 centimeters long
were produced in Germany at one time, but only in limited
quantities.

Many millions of carats of artificial gems are now produced
each year, mostly by the Verneuil process which has been worked
successfully in France, Germany, Italy, Switzerland, and more
recently, in the U.S.A.; the art of growing the boules has been
brought to such a pitch that one operator can attend to a whole
battery of crystallizers. Not all the stones are intended for
adornment; considerable quantities of corundum crystals are
used as jewel bearings in watches and electric meters—they are
more uniform and reliable than the natural crystals. Quite
small stones are, of course, adequate for such purposes: they
were at first made by cutting up the boules, but less cutting is
required if the corundum is grown as a thin rod having just the
right diameter, so that it is only necessary to slice it into sections.

Not unnaturally, there have been many attempts to grow
diamonds; this has undoubtedly been done, but at the cost of
prodigious efforts which have so far produced only very minute
stones. Towards the end of the last century several attempts
were made by various methods—for instance, by suddenly
quenching a solution of carbon in molten iron and then dissolving
away the iron by acid, or by heating carbon compounds with
various other substances to high temperatures at high pressures;
but though it was claimed that very small black diamonds were
made by more than one method, these claims were never sub-
stantiated. It is not certain that diamonds were ever obtained
by these methods. Success came at last in 1955, when the General
Electric Company in the U.S.A. produced authentic diamonds;
they are not clear "gem quality" crystals, but only small black
"industrial quality" ones, but the success is a considerable
technical achievement; moreover, it has been developed into a
commercial process. Success was achieved by using extremely
high pressures—something like a million and a half pounds per

square inch (a good deal higher than any pressure attained previously)—as well as high temperatures. Graphite or some other form of carbon, mixed with tantalum metal, is compressed, and the temperature is then raised to 1600°C to melt the metal and give the carbon atoms enough mobility to change their arrangement. The temperature is then lowered to freeze in the new structure, and finally the pressure is released. The point is that since diamond is denser than other forms of carbon, very high pressures encourage its formation, and provided that the new structure is frozen in, by lowering the temperature, it will not revert to graphite when the pressure is released. The diamonds made in this way are small black ones, not of gem quality; but they are very suitable for some industrial purposes, and are said to be more efficient for grinding purposes than natural diamond grit and command rather higher prices.

Diamonds are used widely in industry for many different types of tools. In addition to glass cutters and engraving tools, there are drills, particularly core bits for rock drills used in drilling for oil and minerals; these are tubes armed with diamonds at the lower edge. Then there are diamond dies for wire drawing (diamonds with tapered holes through them), diamond styli for gramophone recording heads and pickups, and finally diamond bearings for high class electric meters and chronometers. For the last mentioned applications, diamond bearings outlast corundum bearings many times; it is said that in one test 57% of corundum (ruby) bearings were useless after one million revolutions, but with diamond bearings there were no signs of wear after 25 million revolutions.

The very high pressure process by which diamonds are made has had other successes. Another substance has been discovered which is comparable with diamond in hardness. This is borazon, a crystal having the same arrangement of atoms as diamond but containing boron and nitrogen atoms in equal numbers instead of carbon atoms. It is said to be very similar to diamond in hardness, but superior to it in thermal stability and resistance to oxidation; if so, it should find useful applications. Probably other new crystal species will be discovered by the use of this newly accessible range of very high pressures. The pressure–temperature cycle used is one that does not normally occur in nature; when material is brought from the depths of the earth, as diamonds are thought to have been brought, pressure and temperature fall together, and crystals formed at high pressure and temperature are liable to revert to more normal species. It appears to be a lucky accident that natural diamonds have survived at all. Our ability to control temperature and pressure independently may well lead to further new discoveries.

Plates 1-15

PLATE 1.   A group of quartz crystals. One-quarter actual size. [By permission of the British Museum (Natural History).]

PLATE 2. Two photographs of very small crystals, taken by the electron microscope. Individual molecules are clearly visible. *Above:* protein from southern bean mosaic virus. Magnification 30,000. *Below:* protein from tobacco necrosis virus. Magnification 73,000. Photographs by R. W. G. Wyckoff.

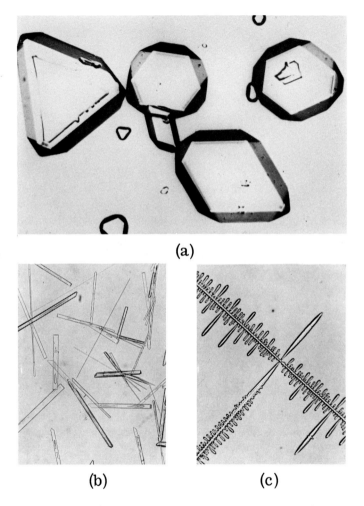

(a)

(b)   (c)

PLATE 3. Crystals grown from solution. (a) Lead nitrate. (b) Urea, from strongly supersaturated solution. (c) Ammonium chloride.

PLATE 4. Crystal of Rothamsted necrosis protein, showing layers one molecule thick, which look as if they have grown outward from the center of the face. Electron microscope photograph by R. W. G. Wyckoff. Magnification 50,000.

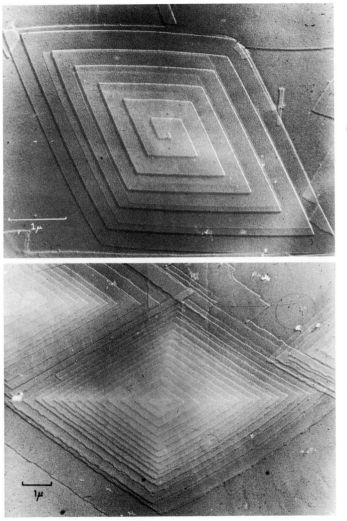

(a)

(b)

PLATE 5. Crystals of the paraffin hydrocarbon hectane, showing (a) spiral layer formation originating from a single screw dislocation, (b) concentric layer growth originating from a pair of opposite (left- and right-hand) dislocations. Electron microscope photographs by I.M. Dawson. Magnifications 15,000 and 7,500, respectively.

PLATE 6. Snowflakes. Photographs by W. A. Bentley. [From W.A. Bentley and W.J. Humphries, "Snow Crystals." McGraw-Hill, New York (1931). Used by permission.]

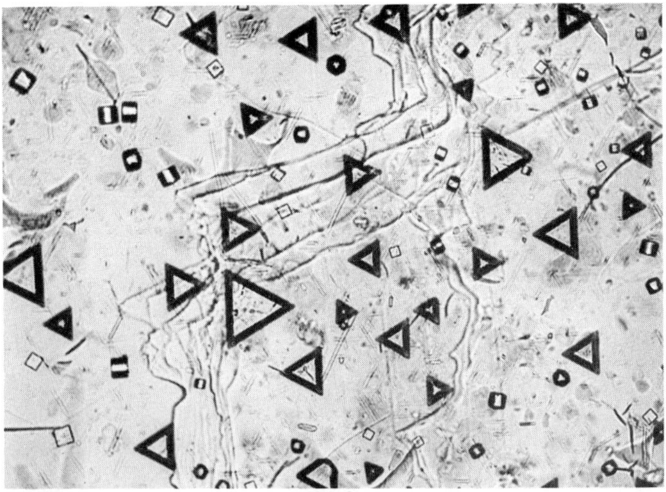

PLATE 7. Ammonium iodide crystals growing, precisely oriented, on cleavage surfaces of mica. (a) On phlogopite mica the triangular ammonium iodide crystals grow in two orientations indiscriminately. (b) On lepidolite mica the triangles are all the same way up on an atomically perfect cleavage surface, and the opposite way up if the cleavage happens to occur at another level of the mica structure where the pattern is reversed. In this specimen there is evidently an invisible step from one level to another.

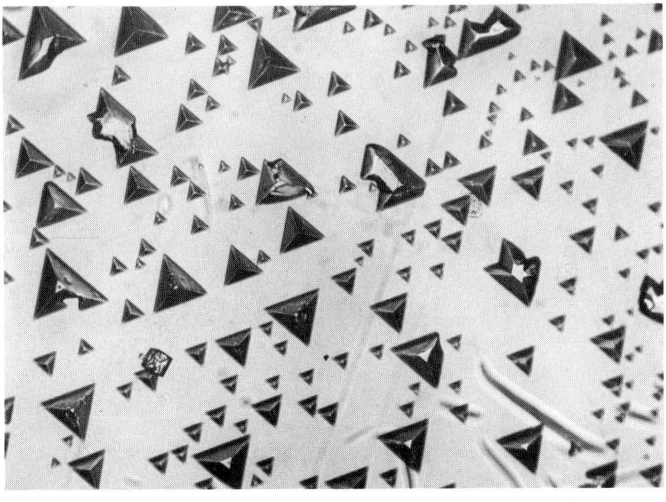

PLATE 8. A thin layer of crystallized polythene, photographed under the microscope between crossed polarizers. A dark cross on an illuminated ground is evidence of a radial arrangement of tiny crystals; each radial unit is known as a spherulite. Magnification 500.

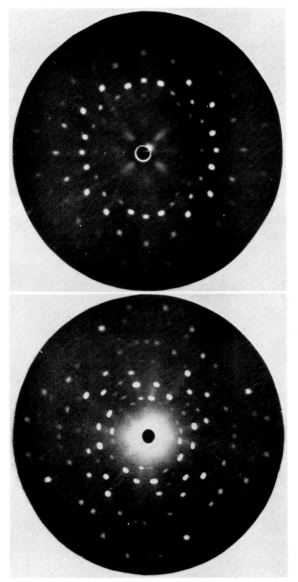

PLATE 9. Laue diffraction patterns given by ammonium chloride *(above)* and pentaerythritol *(below)*. X-ray beam along fourfold axis of symmetry. The patterns show clearly the fourfold symmetry; they also show that in ammonium chloride there are planes of symmetry parallel to the fourfold axis, while in pentaerythritol there are not.

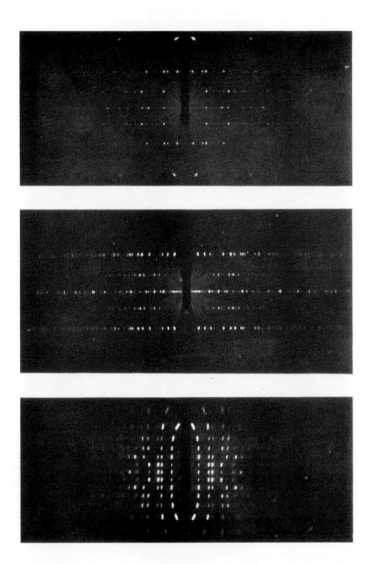

PLATE 10. X-ray diffraction patterns recorded on cylindrical films with monochromatic X-rays. *Above:* potassium nitrate. *Center:* gypsum. *Below:* benzil.

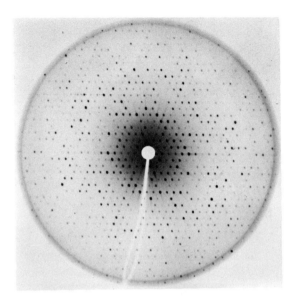

PLATE 11. An X-ray diffraction pattern of a crystal of hemoglobin, taken by an ingenious goniometer camera known as a "precession camera."

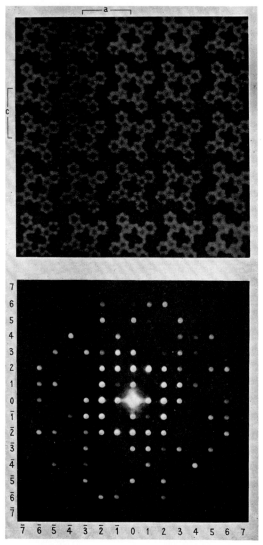

PLATE 12. *Above:* a pattern representing the structure of the phthalocyanine crystal, seen along a particular direction. *Below:* the optical
diffraction pattern given by it; this corresponds closely to the X-ray
diffraction pattern given by the real crystal.

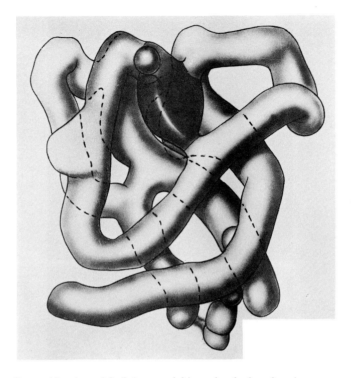

PLATE 13. A model of the myoglobin molecule, based on interpretation of X-ray diffraction patterns given by the crystal. This model shows the general configuration of the protein chain. Detailed results show that the straight portions consist of the helical chains shown in Fig. 121; elsewhere the chain has a less regular configuration. The dark disk is the heme group, the oxygen carrier; the little balls show the positions of the heavy atoms which were put in to make it possible to work out the structure. About twenty million times actual size.

PLATE 14. (a) An electron microscope photograph of an insect virus particle (adenovirus). (b) A packing of spheres to demonstrate the structure more clearly. This structure is not a crystal, for it has fivefold axes of symmetry; it is a supermolecule, in which an outer shell of protein molecules encloses a core of nucleate. About 700,000 times actual size. Photograph by K.W. Horne.

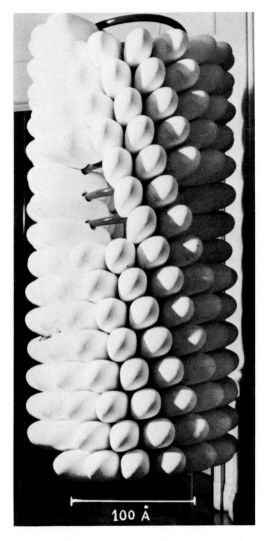

100 Å

PLATE 15. A model of the structure of a particle of tobacco mosaic virus: a supermolecule having protein units attached to a helical nucleate chain. Some protein units have been removed to reveal the nucleate chain. About three million times actual size.

STRUCTURE AND INTERACTION
WITH LIGHT AND X-RAYS

CHAPTER 9

The Play of Light

In this chapter I am not going to deal with those effects of light which are of essentially the same nature in crystals as in other forms of matter like glass or water: effects like the bending of light when it goes from air into glass or water (the behavior which makes a stick look bent when it is dipping into water, and which makes it possible to construct lenses for spectacles and cameras), and the splitting of white light into a rainbow band of colors by glass prisms and by rain drops in the air. Crystals do these things just as glass does, and some of them, especially diamonds, do them with even more striking effects. Colored crystals, too, have a beauty of their own: the addition of color to the already remarkable shapes enhances their attractiveness. But these are what we can call normal effects of light because they are shown by all substances, whether crystalline or not. What I want to deal with now are some strange effects which occur in crystals but not in liquids or glasses, except in very special circumstances; they are essentially crystal effects, because they are due to the orderly pattern of atoms in the crystals.

The first sign of something very odd is seen by simply making a small mark like a cross on a piece of paper and putting a crystal of calcite (a cleavage rhomb) on it so that you are looking at the cross through the crystal; you will see not one cross but two (Fig. 70a). (There are demonstrations of this effect in most museums which have collections of minerals.) There is no doubt about it—there are two crosses side by side, both of them sharp and clear; and if you rotate the crystal while still resting it on the paper on top of the cross, one of the images keeps still as one would expect, while the other rotates around it, keeping pace with the crystal, as you twist it (Fig. 71). In other words, one image seems to behave normally (as it would if you saw it through a piece of glass), but the other is quite extraordinary. The ordinary image is produced in your eye by rays of light which come through the crystal in the same way as through glass—if you are looking straight down at the paper, the rays are not bent but come straight through; but the extraordinary image is produced by rays which, even if you are looking straight down at the paper, are bent sideways (see Fig. 70b)—that is

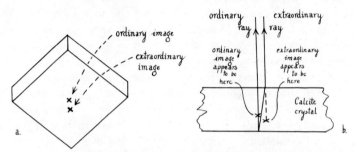

FIG. 70. The mystery of the double cross. (a) Seen through a calcite crystal, a single cross appears double. (b) Paths of light rays through the crystal.

why the extraordinary cross appears at the side of the ordinary one. If you are not looking straight down, both rays are bent, but to different degrees. There is one other important difference between the two images; both of them look higher than the paper, as anything does if seen through glass or water (a stick

FIG. 71. When the calcite crystal is rotated, the ordinary image stays still, but the extraordinary image rotates with the crystal.

partly in water looks bent, and its lower end looks higher than it really is), but the ordinary image looks higher than the extra-ordinary one. The reason for the false appearances of depth when things are seen through glass or water is, of course, the bending of the light rays when they pass from the glass or water into air; the degree of bending is expressed in what is called the refractive index—the higher the refractive index, the more the bending; glass has a higher refractive index than water, and the apparent thickness of a piece of thick glass when you look through it is less than the apparent thickness of the same depth of water. So, to return to the two images seen through a calcite crystal, the fact that the two images seem to be at different depths means that the calcite crystal behaves as if it has two different refractive indices: there are two rays coming through, and the refractive index for the ordinary one is greater than for the extraordinary one. It certainly seems very odd for a substance to behave as if it were two different substances at one and the same time; yet that is undoubtedly what happens.

No wonder that these strange effects, when they were first noticed in the seventeenth century, excited the greatest amazement among the few who knew about them. They were first described in 1669 by Erasmus Bartholinus, a Danish professor of mathematics and medicine, who wrote this: "Greatly prized by all men is the diamond, and many are the joys which similar treasures bring, such as precious stones and pearls, though they serve only for decoration and adornment of the finger and the neck; but he who on the other hand prefers the knowledge of unusual phenomena to these delights, he will I hope have no less joy in a new sort of body, namely a transparent crystal, recently brought to us from Iceland, which perhaps is one of the greatest wonders that nature has produced."

Iceland spar or calcite is certainly a remarkable crystal, but since the time of Bartholinus we have learnt that it is not really exceptional in its optical properties. Most crystals affect light in the same sort of way, giving two refracted rays; in fact, all except cubic crystals behave in this way (provided of course that they are transparent), though in most of them the effects are not so striking. It depends on the difference between the two refractive indices, and in calcite it happens that the difference is larger than in many other crystals, so that the two images of the cross are better separated. The crystallographer's name for the phenomenon is "double refraction" or, if you want a single word, "birefringence."

But there are even more curious things to come. William Nicol in 1828 devised a way of getting rid of one of the rays, the ordinary one. Never mind for the moment how it is done—it is a matter of cutting the crystal at a particular angle and reflecting the ordinary ray away—but accept the fact that only the extra-ordinary ray is left. If we have two crystals treated in this way —Nicol prisms, as they are called (they are fitted to many microscopes)— and play with them, some remarkable things happen; if you look through both prisms at a lamp (so that the light from the lamp—or a window, for that matter—goes through first one prism and then the other on its way to your eye), and rotate one of the prisms (it does not matter which), you find that for certain positions no light gets through at all; as you rotate the prism, the light becomes gradually stronger, then fades again to nothing, brightens again, and so on. Each prism, if used by itself, seems normal: you can see the light through it, and rotation of the prism makes no difference; but if both are used together and one is rotated, there is alternate light and darkness, and the position for complete darkness is at right angles to the position for maximum lightness (Fig. 72). The light that gets through a Nicol prism must be very abnormal in some way, since a second prism (which looks just as transparent as the first) is able to stop it completely.

The explanation for these odd facts is bound up with the nature of light. Ordinary light consists of waves: there is something vibrating, and the rapid advance of a ray of light is due to the rapid spreading of the vibrations; but—and this is the important point—the vibrations are not along the direction of travel of the ray (as sound vibrations are), but at right angles to the direction of travel; they are known as "transverse vibrations." There are all sorts of directions at right angles to the ray direction (just as a stretched guitar string can vibrate sideways or outwards from the instrument or in any intermediate direction, depending on the direction of plucking), and in ordinary light from a lamp there are vibrations in all the possible planes at right angles to the ray direction; but the light that gets through

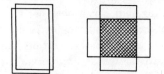

FIG. 72. Two Nicol prisms, or two polaroid sheets, transmit light when parallel, but stop it completely when crossed.

a Nicol prism vibrates in only one plane: it is called "polarized light" (Fig. 73). The behavior of a second Nicol prism in line with the first will obviously depend on whether its transmission plane is parallel to the transmission plane of the first; if it is,

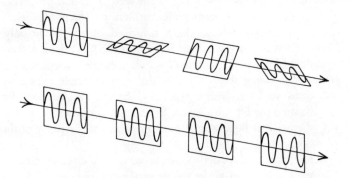

FIG. 73. Ordinary light (*above*) and polarized light (*below*).

the light gets through, but if the transmission planes are exactly crossed (exactly at right angles to each other), the light is completely stopped.

So far, so good; but there is one more thing to explain: it is evident from the *gradual* fading in and out as the Nicol prism is rotated that at intermediate positions part of the light gets through. You might think that if the Nicol prism only lets through light vibrating in one plane, the second prism would have to have its transmission plane *exactly* in line with that of the first in order to let any light through at all. But evidently that is not the right way to think about it; the situation is more like that of a sailing ship which does not have to move exactly in the direction of the wind but can, by the use of sail and rudder, move at almost any angle by using *part* of the force of the wind. The accepted word for this is "resolution"; the ship uses the "resolved part" of the force of the wind in the direction in which it wants to travel, and the Nicol prism lets through the "resolved part" of the incoming light, the part resolved into its own transmission plane. The complete stopping of the light when the two Nicol prisms are crossed is due to the fact that the light from the first prism has no component in the transmission plane of the second prism; the "resolved part" is in these circumstances zero.

Nicol's ingenious device has proved extremely useful in all sorts of ways; in fact, the study of the strange optical properties of crystals would be impossible without the help of such a device which lets through light polarized in one plane only. Nowadays it is possible to use, instead of a Nicol prism, a sheet of material known as "Polaroid" which does the same thing but succeeds in doing it by a rather different principle which we will come to later. Either type of polarizer can be used for investigating the light which comes through crystals, and finding out whether it is polarized or not, and which is the plane of the vibrations.

Return now to the calcite crystal resting on a cross marked on a piece of paper, and to the puzzle of the two crosses which can be seen through the crystal. If you look through a polarizer at the two crosses, and rotate the polarizer, you will see that at one position one of the crosses disappears, and then on rotating further reappears again; but at the same time the other cross begins to fade, and at a position at right angles to the extinction position of the first, it in turn disappears. On continued rotation, the two crosses extinguish alternately, at positions mutually at right angles (Fig. 74). Evidently the two rays coming through the crystal are both polarized, but the plane of vibration of the ordinary ray is at right angles to that of the extraordinary ray. The two planes of vibration are naturally closely related to the structure of the crystal: the ordinary ray vibrates in a plane bisecting the acute angles of the cleavage rhomb of calcite, while the plane of vibration of the extraordinary ray bisects the obtuse angles. The arrangement of atoms is quite different in these two directions; the light selects the principal directions for its vibrations, and since the refractive index depends on the arrangement of atoms in the plane of vibration (it is not the direction of travel of the light, but the vibration direction, that matters), the refractive indices of the two rays are quite different. This is why the crystal behaves in a sense as if it were two different substances simultaneously: it is because its structure in one principal direction is quite different from its structure in the

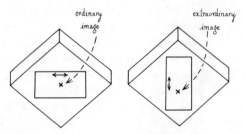

Fig. 74. A Nicol prism or a polaroid sheet, when its vibration plane bisects the acute angle of the cleavage rhomb (*left*), transmits only the ordinary image; when its vibration plane bisects the obtuse angle of the crystal (*right*), it transmits only the extraordinary image.

other principal direction at right angles to the first, and so it has two different refractive indices simultaneously. All this comes from the fact that light consists of transverse vibrations.

This then is the solution of the mystery of the double cross. Firstly, the crystal has the power of converting ordinary light into two rays, both plane polarized but with their planes of vibration at right angles to each other; secondly, the refractive index of the ordinary ray is very different from that of the extraordinary ray (that is why the two crosses appear to be at different depths); and thirdly the laws of refraction or bending are different for the two rays (the ordinary ray behaves in the same way as in glass or water, but the extraordinary ray bends abnormally according to special rules of its own).

All this, though it may seem rather strange, fits perfectly well into a coherent scheme of ideas. Nowadays, with the benefits of hundreds of years of thought and experiment behind us, we are able to give a straightforward and consistent account of these remarkable properties of crystals. But our present clear picture was only attained after a long and difficult struggle to sort out the facts and think out what they mean; in fact, it took some of the clearest heads in scientific history to get it clear. It is worth while to look back at the state of knowledge in the early years of the nineteenth century, when it was beginning to come clear, because the development of ideas at that time forms a striking example of the way in which the jigsaw puzzle of facts and ideas takes shape—how queer-shaped pieces turn up which, inserted by clear and discerning minds, justify and complete a structure laboriously and hopefully built up by others.

You will notice that in my simplified account of the play of light in a calcite crystal I have taken for granted certain very fundamental ideas—the wave nature of light, and the idea that the vibrations of light are not along the direction of travel of the light but at right angles to it (the accepted name for them is "transverse vibrations"). But these things were by no means clear 150 years ago; if they had been, it would have been much easier to understand the optical properties of crystals. As a matter of fact, it was the optical properties of crystals which helped to clarify them; what the natural philosophers of the time had to do was to solve several problems simultaneously, because only by fitting in the various separate pieces of the jig-saw was the whole design clear.

The nature of light has been, throughout scientific history, one of the most difficult things to understand: light, one of the most essential conditions of our existence, has always been much harder to understand in terms of common sense ideas than matter. In Sir Isaac Newton's time, just before 1700, there were two rival theories. One of them, strongly advocated by the Dutchman Christian Huygens, maintained that light is a kind of wave motion; he is said to have gotten his first ideas on wave motion by watching the behavior of ripples on a Dutch canal. Huygens was able to give a very good account of the two images seen through a calcite crystal by considering the advance of wave fronts and assuming that for some reason or other there were two different sorts of wave fronts advancing through the crystal. But although he discovered something about polarization by experiments with two crystals, he did not explain it, so the account remained incomplete. He must have been a very remarkable man, for he came close to understanding things which were only cleared up over a century later: on the basis of his observations of ripples, he realized that two sets of waves could interfere with each other—annihilating each other at some places and building up to greater amplitudes at others—and that if light is a wave motion this sort of thing ought to happen to light waves. But interference of light had not been seen at the time; moreover, if light was a wave motion what did it vibrate in? It was known that light goes through a vacuum just as well as through air or glass; if there was something in the vacuum to sustain the vibrations, it would have to have the most remarkable properties. Most people could not swallow the notion, and Newton himself favored the idea that light consists of a stream of particles of some sort.

There the matter rested for a century and, probably on account of the enormous prestige of Newton's name, the particle theory held the field. But in 1800 Thomas Young, an English physician, in a paper to the Royal Society, respectfully but firmly rejected the particle theory and, on the basis of his own experiments, claimed to have demonstrated the interference of light that was required by Huygens' wave theory. Young was a man of great ability and very wide interests; after an extremely precocious childhood (he was said to have read completely through the Bible twice when four years old), he became a classical scholar, knew several languages and made contributions to philology, and was one of the first to have some success in deciphering ancient

Egyptian hieroglyphic inscriptions; all this in addition to being
a physician and making many vital contributions to physics.
His crucial experiment on the nature of light (Fig. 75) was to
show that the light from a single minute source, coming through
two tiny pinholes very close together (in any opaque screen),
forms a pattern such as could be produced by the reinforcement
of the light in some places and cancellation in others—precisely
the sort of interference pattern required by the wave theory.
The reason why interference had not been seen before was that
the wavelength of light is extremely small, so that very refined
methods are necessary to detect the pattern: the source of light
must be extremely tiny (a minute pinhole in a screen) and the
two pinholes for the experiment must be very small and very
close together, preferably less than a millimeter.

In spite of this demonstration, many people still found it
difficult to accept the wave theory; in fact, it was openly ridiculed
by some. It was said that the effects of the light striking the

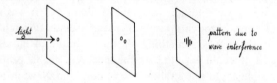

FIG. 75.   Thomas Young's experiment.

edges of the pinholes might have been responsible for the pattern;
and the medium for the waves to vibrate in—whatever there is
in a vacuum—would have to have enormous elasticity to permit
very rapid vibrations, combined with very low density to allow
a very high velocity—properties completely outside the range
of those of any known substances, let alone a vacuum supposed
to be empty. The silencing of the objections to the pinhole
experiment, as well as the submitting of some of the new evidence
which finally established the wave theory, was largely the work
of the Frenchman, Augustin Fresnel, who started life as an
engineer but later turned to the study of light. In his first
experiments he repeated, quite independently, Young's experi-

ments on interference; when his attention was drawn to Young's work he wrote to Young, in spite of the fact that it was in 1815, the year of the battle of Waterloo, and this started a correspondence kept up until Fresnel's death in 1827. It is pleasant to recall that their relations were never marred by controversy, but were always on the friendly basis of mutual interests and the generous recognition of each other's achievements. Fresnel demonstrated interference by methods utilizing mirrors and prisms, where there was no question of pinhole edge effects. This time there was no escape from the wave theory, and, however preposterous the properties of whatever there was in a vacuum, they had to be accepted.

The other big idea—the idea of transverse vibrations—was only slowly realized by both Young and Fresnel. They thought of vibrations along the direction of travel like sound waves, and hardly dared to propose transverse vibrations. The reason for their doubts was that while it is easy to imagine vibrations along the direction of travel being transmitted by a series of pressure waves as sound is, sideways vibrations appeared to demand a medium with the rigidity of a solid: a rope transmits sideways vibrations but it is hard to imagine a gas doing so, and still more difficult to credit a vacuum with such a power. Eventually, however, the evidence forced them to accept the idea of transverse vibrations.

Really convincing evidence only came with the study of polarized light and of the properties of crystals. Interest in these subjects was revived by the work of another Frenchman, Etienne Malus, who one day in 1808 was looking through a calcite crystal at the reflection of the sun in a window of the Luxembourg palace in Paris; he saw two images, and noticed that when he rotated the crystal the two images faded and intensified alternately. This set him experimenting with reflections at different angles, and he found that by careful adjustment of a reflecting glass plate at a particular angle, he could make each of the images seen through the crystal disappear completely —not both at once but alternately; as the crystal was rotated, first one image would disappear, and then, after 90° rotation, the other (while the first had meanwhile strengthned to full intensity). This is exactly the same result as I described earlier in this chapter as given by a Nicol prism or Polaroid sheet; but there were no Nicol prisms or Polaroid sheets in those days.

Evidently light reflected by glass is, as we say, polarized, but only completely polarized if the angle of reflection is just right. (As a matter of fact, all polished surfaces of transparent materials behave in this way). The fact that the two images seen through the crystal disappeared at crystal positions 90° apart obviously meant that, whatever is the nature of polarized light, the two images are due to rays whose polarization has something to do with directions at right angles to each other.

The importance of the discovery of polarization by reflection was that it provided a ready method of polarization, before the invention of the Nicol prism; it opened the way to the study of crystal properties, and to all sorts of experiments with polarized light. Perhaps the most important of these was Fresnel's discovery that two beams from the same source, polarized at right angles, do not produce an interference pattern, whereas similarly polarized beams do. This could only mean that light consists of transverse vibrations, that polarization is the restriction of the vibrations to one plane, and that oppositely polarized beams have their vibrations in planes which are at right angles to each other. However difficult it was to credit a vacuum with the necessary rigidity, transverse vibrations had to be accepted. Evidently the mechanical analogies were not applicable to light.

In this way the peculiar properties of crystals played an important part in revealing the nature of light itself. From that time on, the wave theory was firmly established; and when, later on in the nineteenth century, it was shown that light travels more slowly through liquid and solid substances than through air, it seemed that the last nail had been driven into the coffin of the particle theory (which, to explain refraction, required light to travel *faster* in liquids and solids). Ironically enough, this is not the end of the story of the nature of light. It is as far as we need go in dealing with the behavior of light in crystals; but it would not be right to leave the subject without mentioning that in the twentieth century the idea of a particle of light has reappeared. It has been forced on us by certain properties of light which were unknown in the days of Young and Fresnel: the laws of radiation of light forced Max Planck reluctantly to the conclusion that light is released in short bursts, of magnitude controlled absolutely by the frequency, and the facts about the production of electrons when light strikes certain metals led Einstein to conclude that the absorption of light similarly takes place only in the same definite quantities. In fact, light appears to exist only in short bursts (called quanta or photons) of fixed size. To accept this is not to abandon the wave theory; far from it—the facts about interference and polarization are so perfectly explained by the wave theory that the abandonment of it is unthinkable; what we have to do is to accept both conceptions, and to imagine a particle or photon of light as a short burst of waves, which in some circumstances exhibits typical wavelike behavior but in others appears to behave more like a particle. A photon is a system of waves which spreads out from the source, and thus behaves as if it has extension in space; yet when it interacts with matter, as when it strikes a silver bromide grain in a photographic plate, the whole of its energy is concentrated at a point.

As a matter of fact, for all interference phenomena, the quantum of light or photon raises very strange difficulties; for it appears that interference does not take place between *different* photons—everything happens within one photon. But if a photon is indivisible, what happens when one of them goes through two holes at once to produce interference on the other side, as in Young's famous experiment, doesn't bear thinking about; at any rate, we cannot form a physical picture of the process in any common sense way. Indeed, it looks as if we are perpetrating a logical contradiction by saying first that a photon is indivisible and then that it *is* divisible. Nevertheless the facts force us to this apparent contradiction. This is a glimpse of that strange and rather terrifying world in which ordinary imagination fails, and we have to learn to accept totally new ways of thought; but fortunately it is not necessary to take more than a glimpse of it, for in crystal optics the wave aspect of light is dominant, and we can get on perfectly well (in fact, far better) without thinking about the photon.

As for the other awkward question that bothered the pioneers in the nineteenth century—"What is it that vibrates, what is the medium the light waves are waving in, what is there in a vacuum?"—this question has had a long history of puzzled speculation and argument, but now seems destined for the shelf. The medium, with its enormous elasticity but no "material" properties like density, was for a long time called the "ether," and indeed the word still reappears occasionally. But all attempts to find evidence for its existence apart from space itself and to detect the motion of the earth through a supposed stationary "ether" have failed, and since the acceptance of Einstein's theories there seems to be no point in talking about "ether" at all. Light is something that happens in "empty" space; if "ether" is everywhere that space is, there is no sense in dragging in the extra word at all; we might as well say that the ability to sustain light waves is a property of space and have done with it. Light waves, we know now, are electromagnetic in character; very well then, let us say that it is a property of space to carry electromagnetic waves. In Einstein's theories light has the character of an "absolute"—something quite fundamental that just has to be accepted. Shall we ever get behind it to something more fundamental? At one time it looked as if atoms were "absolutes," but we have now realized that they are composed of more fundamental entities; will the same story be repeated with light?

So much for the fundamentals. Let us now return to the rhombohedral calcite crystal resting on a piece of paper with a cross on it. To look through a rhombohedron placed in this way is to look through the atomic arrangement in a particular direction—a direction which is not a principal direction of the structure, not a symmetry axis. It is true that the behavior of the light depends, not on the arrangement of atoms in the direction of travel of the light, but on the arrangements in the vibration directions which are at right angles (transverse) to the ray direction; nevertheless the arrangements of atoms in the transverse directions vary as one changes the direction of travel, consequently if one looked through a calcite crystal in quite a different direction one would expect to see something different. To tilt the crystal would be to introduce refraction effects, which would be confusing, and the best way of investigating the matter is to use a differently shaped crystal. Calcite crystals grow in various shapes; some are hexagonal prisms, and if such a crystal is laid on the paper, resting on one of the prism faces, it appears at first sight that there is only one cross; but a closer examination shows that there are really two images at different apparent depths, one on top of the other; and a test with a Nicol prism or a polaroid sheet shows that they are, as before, polarized at right angles—they disappear in turn as the polarizer is rotated. Evidently much the same sort of thing is happening, except that for this orientation of the crystal structure the extraordinary ray is not bent abnormally. Other aspects of the crystal are not so readily investigated because there are not always suitable natural faces for the crystal to rest on (and tilting brings in other refraction effects which confuse the issue); but out of large crystals, parallel-sided blocks can be cut in any orientation. I shall mention only one other orientation—the very special aspect in which one is looking along the prism axis, the axis of trigonal symmetry. In this position, only one cross can be seen; it really is only one, and a test with a polarizer shows that the image is not polarized, for it remains unchanged when the polarizer is rotated.

All this was known to Huygens before 1700, and he realized that there is only this one direction in which a crystal like calcite behaves simply and normally like glass; in all other directions there are two images and two refractive indices, but the difference between the two refractive indices, as well as the amount of abnormal bending of the extraordinary ray, depend on the direction in which one is looking. The ordinary ray always has the same refractive index, but that of the extraordinary ray varies. Its lowest value (in calcite it is always lower than that of the ordinary ray) is when one is looking along a direction at right angles to the trigonal axis (as for the hexagonal prism resting on a prism face); for all other directions it has an intermediate value. As one approaches the trigonal axis, the extraordinary refractive index approaches the ordinary one, until, when one looks straight along the trigonal axis, the two are indistinguishable, and there is only one image, just as there is through glass.

There is another way of investigating the refractive indices of crystals which is worth describing here because the phenomena involved bring out the peculiarities of crystals in a way which is striking in itself and different from the "double cross" experiment. This method depends on an extremely simple principle—that if you put a colorless transparent object in a colorless liquid having exactly the same refractive index, the outlines of the solid object cannot be seen at all: the light goes straight through without (so to speak) knowing that it is going through two different substances. (Refractive index is to light what density is to gravitation: a solid object in a liquid of the same density neither floats nor sinks, but stays anywhere—gravity, so to speak, does not know that there are two different things there.) The method is much used for small crystals under the microscope, but it works just the same on any other scale; it is capable of giving fairly accurate results.

The ordinary refractive index of calcite is 1.658; if a crystal is put into a liquid of this same refractive index and illuminated by plane polarized light vibrating in the crystal's own vibration direction for the ordinary ray, it will be invisible (or rather, not quite invisible, for, if white light is used, faint color bands will probably be seen around the edges, because the refractive indices of liquid and crystal will match for one color but will not quite match for other colors). If now the polarizer is rotated through a right angle so that it supplies light vibrating in the direction for the extraordinary ray, the crystal becomes very plainly visible, and in fact shows up in strong relief. By rotating the polarizer, the crystal can be made to appear or disappear at will. The extraordinary refractive index can be measured by keeping the polarizer in the appropriate position and trying other liquids until invisibility is achieved for *this* vibration direction.

The crystal can now be tilted into various other orientations and the experiments repeated; it is found that the ordinary refractive index is always the same, but the extraordinary refractive index varies, and is lowest when the crystal is viewed in a direction at right angles to the trigonal axis. When one looks straight *along* the trigonal axis, the two indices become one, and this is equal to the ordinary index; for this aspect the crystal is invisible in a liquid of refractive index 1.658, and rotation of the polarizer makes no difference.

With the revival of interest in polarized light in the early years of the nineteenth century, and the increased facilities for studying it, other types of crystals were examined, and the relations between their optical properties and their symmetry were discovered. First of all, it must be mentioned that no crystal of cubic symmetry shows any of the remarkable effects seen in calcite; light goes through a cubic crystal in exactly the same way as through glass or water: there is no polarization and no double refraction, in whatever direction one looks through the crystal. One can easily see why this is so, at any rate for the principal directions: if one looks along a unit cell edge, the arrangements of atoms in any two directions at right angles to the line of vision and at right angles to each other are precisely the same, so the two refractive indices associated with these directions are the same. But all other crystals show double refraction in varying degrees, provided of course that they are transparent.

All crystals of trigonal or hexagonal symmetry have the same general characteristics as calcite: there is just one direction of ordinary single refraction—the trigonal or hexagonal axis—and for other directions the difference between the two indices follows the same law of variation as in calcite; but the magnitudes of the indices and the maximum difference between them are different for each crystal species—it depends on the atomic arrangement; and it is not always the ordinary ray which has the higher index—again this depends on the atomic arrangement. It is only the law of variation with direction which is constant. All tetragonal crystals likewise have precisely the same general characteristics and the same law of variation. Because there is only one direction of ordinary single refraction (which coincides always with the unique axis of tetragonal, trigonal, or hexagonal symmetry), all these crystals are described as optically uniaxial. The law of variation is quite a simple one: if one imagines lines radiating from a point, each having a length proportional to the refractive index for that vibration direction, the ends of the lines lie on the surface of a solid figure which has the shape known as an "ellipsoid of revolution"—the shape you would get if you took an ellipse and rotated it about one of its principal axes (see Fig. 76). It is like a sphere which has been either

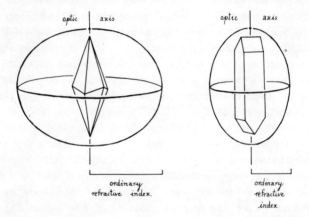

FIG. 76. Representation of variation of refractive index with vibration direction, in an optically negative crystal, calcite (*left*), and an optically positive crystal, urea (*right*).

squashed or pulled out in one direction, so that only one section through the center remains circular, all the others being ellipses. The unique direction of single refraction (which coincides with the unique axis of the crystal) is the direction at right angles to the one circular section; this direction, by the way, is called the "optic axis," and crystals of this type are called "uniaxial" because they have only one optic axis. The radius of the one circular section represents the ordinary refractive index. For all other directions the section at right angles to the ray direction is an ellipse, and the longest and shortest radii of the ellipse represent the two refractive indices for the ray direction in question. One of them is inevitably equal to the radius of the one circular section; that is why the ordinary refractive index is always the same, whatever the direction of travel of the light. Calcite, which has its ordinary refractive index higher than its extraordinary, is known as a negatively birefringent crystal; those which have the ordinary refractive index lower than the extraordinary (urea is an example) are known as positively birefringent. (See again Fig. 76.)

All the "uniaxial" crystals are quite high in the scale of symmetry; the less symmetrical crystals, as we might expect, have still more varied optical characteristics. For most aspects they are doubly refracting, and this time *both* rays are extraordinary in the sense that they are bent abnormally. The most concise way of summing up their optical characteristics is to say that the solid figure which represents the way in which refractive index varies with vibration direction is, for these less symmetrical crystals, not an ellipsoid of revolution but an ellipsoidal figure having all three of its principal dimensions unequal (Fig. 77). This means several things. In the first place, consider a crystal of orthorhombic symmetry like sodium carbonate monohydrate, which is illustrated in Fig. 78; if we look through the crystal in the three principal directions in turn, there are two refractive indices for each aspect, but no one value is constant for all three aspects (as it is for the more symmetrical uniaxial types). The three principal dimensions of the ellipsoid are usually labeled with the Greek letters α, β, γ (in order of increasing magnitude), and for each aspect of the crystal we get two of these, but a different pair each time. For one aspect, we get α and β, for another β and γ, and for the third α and γ. In orthorhombic crystals the three principal axes of the ellipsoid coincide with the three principal axes of the crystal, as in Fig. 78, but in monoclinic and triclinic crystals this is not so.

Another consequence of this particular setup of optical characteristics is that in these crystals there are *two* directions of ordinary single refraction: an ellipsoid having all three principal axes unequal has two circular sections (see again Fig. 77), and if light travels along a line perpendicular to either of these circular sections there is no double refraction; the one refractive index is equal to the intermediate principal index, β. The two directions (known as "optic axes") do not correspond to any axial direction

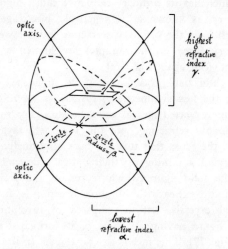

FIG. 77. Representation of variation of refractive index with vibration direction, for crystals of low symmetry ("biaxial" crystals). An ellipsoid with its three principal axes all unequal. The three principal refractive indices are called α, β, γ, in order of increasing magnitude.

in the crystal structure; the directions are determined by the relative magnitudes of the three principal refractive indices, α, β, and γ, and the angle between the two optic axes varies from

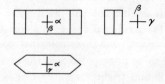

FIG. 78. A crystal of sodium carbonate monohydrate shows a different pair of refractive indices for each principal aspect.

one crystal species to another. Crystals of this type—all crystals of orthorhombic, monoclinic, and triclinic symmetry—are known as "biaxial" crystals because they have two optic axes or special directions of single refraction.

The method of representing the refractive indices for all the possible vibration directions by solid figures (ellipsoids) is particularly satisfying because it unifies a great range of phenomena. Furthermore, we get a better appreciation of the relations between the optical characteristics of different types of crystals: for the least symmetrical crystals the optical properties are represented by the most general type of ellipsoid—one with all three (mutually perpendicular) axes unequal; for the more symmetrical types the ellipsoid takes on a special form in which two of the axes are equal but the third is different; and finally, to complete the picture, the optical properties of the most highly symmetrical crystals—those of the cubic system—are represented by a still more special form of ellipsoid having all its three axes equal—in other words, a sphere, which expresses the fact that the optical properties are the same in all directions.

To close this chapter, I cannot do better than to quote a paragraph from a letter written by Fresnel to Young in 1824: "For a long time that sensibility or that vanity which people call love of glory is much blunted in me. I labor much less to catch the suffrages of the public than to obtain an inward approval which has always been the sweetest reward of my efforts. Without doubt I have often wanted the spur of vanity to excite me to pursue my researches in moments of disgust and discouragement. But all the compliments which I have received never gave me so much pleasure as the discovery of a theoretical truth or the confirmation of a calculation by experiment."

CHAPTER 10

Chromatic Fantasia

Noncrystalline substances like glass and water are capable of producing color effects which, besides being beautiful in themselves, are of great interest and significance for our understanding of the fundamental processes of nature—effects like the rainbow, and the splitting of white light into its constituent colors by a prism. But crystals, just because they have more complex and varied optical characteristics, are much more versatile in producing beautiful and scientifically significant color patterns; indeed, for the student of optical crystallography who spends much of his time looking at crystals through a polarizing microscope, life is "rainbows all the way."

Many of these color effects occur as a result of using a pair of polarizers in a particular way. Microscopes designed for the study of crystalline substances are fitted with two polarizers (either Nicol prisms or Polaroid sheets), one beneath the object stage and the other in the microscope tube or above the eyepiece; any object on the stage is thus between the two polarizers. If the two polarizers are "crossed"—that is, their transmission planes are at right angles to each other—and if there is nothing on the object stage, no light gets through; but doubly refracting crystals on the stage appear to be lit up, often in bright colors, and look particularly attractive seen against the dark background. A flat crystal is uniformly illuminated with the same color all over; but a crystal with beveled edges shows bands of different colors contouring the edges (Fig. 79); evidently the shade of color depends on the thickness.

The explanation of these colors was first given by Young, who, recalling an observation by Chladni that sound travels faster *along* the fibres of a fir tree than *across* them, suggested that the two oppositely polarized rays in the crystal travel at different speeds (because they are vibrating in different structural planes), and consequently get out of step. The two rays do not interfere in the crystal because they are vibrating at right angles to each other, but when they pass through the polarizer which resolves both of them into its own transmission plane, they do interfere. The amount by which the two rays are out of step depends on the frequency—that is, on the color—of the light; and for a particular thickness of crystal, the rays are completely out of step for one particular color, which is therefore completely cut out, leaving the rest of the spectrum. For some other thickness, a different color is cut out, and so the remaining light is of a different color; this is why a beveled edge is contoured by bands of different colors merging into each other.

It was only much later in the nineteenth century that the velocity of light in solid and liquid substances was measured; it was found that the velocity is inversely proportional to the refractive index (the higher the refractive index, the slower the

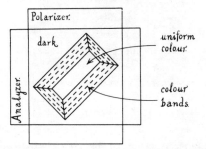

Fig. 79. A birefringent crystal, between crossed polarizers, shows bright colors, the hue depending on the thickness.

light). We have already seen that the two polarized rays in the crystal have different refractive indices; therefore the velocities are different, and since the frequency is not changed, the waves are shorter for the vibration direction of higher refractive index. The difference of wavelength makes it easy to visualize how the two rays get out of step (an attempt is made to depict this in Fig. 80).

The order in which the colors appear on a beveled crystal edge is the same as the order on oil films on a wet road (the colors of which are also due to interference, but produced in this case by the out-of-step relation of the reflections from the upper and lower surfaces of the film). This sequence of colors is known as "Newton's scale," for it was the great Sir Isaac who first described it, having seen it in the colored rings surrounding the point of contact of a lens with a flat glass plate. It is quite different from the sequence in the spectrum given by a prism, or in the rainbow, for each color is produced by the *subtraction* of one color from the complete range—or rather, the complete

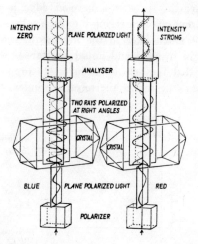

FIG. 80.   Birefringent crystal, between crossed polarizers. For this thickness of crystal, red light is transmitted but blue light is cut out by interference.

subtraction of one precise frequency and partial subtraction of a range of neighboring frequencies. The sequence starts with gray, then comes yellow, then wine red, merging fairly rapidly into peacock blue—these constitute the "first order" (meaning out-of-step relations up to one wavelength); after that we get yellowish-green, yellow, magenta, and violet of the second order (up to two wavelengths phase difference), then emerald green, yellowish and pink of the third order; and thence through alternating, progressively paler shades of green and pink of the higher orders.

The color produced depends not only on the thickness of the crystal but also on the difference between the velocities of the two polarized rays—which is the same as saying the difference between the two refractive indices. If the difference is large—or, as we say, the birefringence is strong—as in calcite, then only an extremely thin crystal will show the brilliant first order colors; thicker ones show the higher order pale greens and pinks, or even white. It is the moderately and weakly birefringent crystals which, in sizes suitable for convenient observation in a low or moderate power microscope, show the most attractive colors. The most spectacular displays are seen when suitable crystals growing from solutions are watched in the polarizing microscope between crossed polarizers: as the thickness increases, the colors change continuously, passing successively through all the stages of Newton's scale. A flat crystal, gray at an early stage, brightens to yellow, begins to show more exciting changes by reddening, and then stages a dramatic early climax by changing fairly suddenly (yet not abruptly but continuously) from wine red to peacock blue; the blue merges into yellowish-green, and then, with ever increasing thickness, there is a series of more delicate changes, through the higher orders of Newton's sequence of colors.

One other fact about these interference colors must be mentioned: the intensity of illumination of the crystal depends on its orientation with respect to the vibration directions of the polarizers; if the microscope stage is rotated (or alternatively the pair of polarizers—microscopes are provided with facilities for doing one or the other), the intensity varies; the crystal extinguishes completely every 90°, and attains maximum brightness midway between the extinction positions. The reason for these changes is that interference colors can only be produced if two oppositely polarized components go through the crystal (to be ultimately united and caused to interfere by being resolved into the upper polarizer's one plane of vibration); and the maximum brightness of interference colors is naturally produced when the two components are of equal intensity. When there is only one component in the crystal, as there is when either of the crystal's vibration directions coincides with that of the lower polarizer, there is no other component to interfere with it; this obviously happens at positions 90° apart; and midway between these positions—that is, when the crystal's vibration directions are at 45° to those of the polarizers—the two components are of equal intensity and produce the brightest interference illumination.

It will be evident that the extinction positions give valuable information in a very simple way—they locate the crystal's vibration planes, provided that those of the polarizers are already known.

Color patterns of quite a different type are produced when a crystal between crossed polarizers is illuminated by strongly convergent light (by a suitable lens just under the microscope stage), and arrangements are made to view, not the ordinary image of the crystal, but the divergent light coming out of the crystal. On polarizing microscopes, there are always arrangements for doing this, for the color patterns so produced give a sort of condensed synopsis of the optical characteristics of the crystal. A calcite crystal, if one looks straight along the principal (trigonal) axis which is also the optical axis, shows a pattern of concentric colored rings with, superimposed on it, a black cross (Fig. 81a). The center of the pattern is dark and corresponds to the optic axis which is the one direction of single refraction in the crystal.

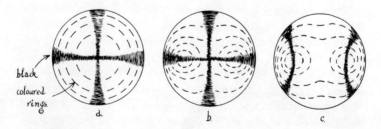

FIG. 81. Convergent light patterns (crossed polarizers). (a) Uniaxial crystal. (b) Biaxial crystal, polarizers thus: +. (c) Biaxial crystal, polarizers thus: ×.

The black cross merely represents the vibration directions of the polarizers: if the polarizers are rotated the cross rotates with them. The concentric colored rings, in which the colors are again arranged in the Newtonian sequence with the highest orders outside, demonstrate the increasing difference between ordinary and extraordinary refractive indices as the direction of travel of the light diverges more and more from the optical axis: in other words, the whole scheme of optical characteristics, which is summarized formally in the ellipsoid (Fig. 76), is demonstrated in a more colorful manner by the convergent light interference figure.

All crystals which are optically uniaxial—that is, all crystals of tetragonal, hexagonal, or trigonal symmetry—give this type of interference figure; but the number of colored rings seen depends on the magnitude of the birefringence of the crystal (the difference between the extreme refractive indices) and on the thickness of the crystal. If the crystal is tilted so that one is not looking straight along the optic axis, the same interference pattern will be seen, but off center. (There are limits, of course: if the crystal is too tilted, the optic axis will be outside the field of view, outside the cone of convergent light.)

Biaxial crystals give a different type of interference figure in which, if the birefringence is great enough and the angle between the optic axes is not too great, two sets of colored rings can be seen, one to each optic axis. The outer rings of each set join up to form loops and (further out still) elliptical rings enclosing both sets. There are also black lines to set off the colors in an artistic way, but the arrangement of them depends on the orientation of the polarizers with respect to the plane of the optic axes; if the vibration direction of one of the polarizers passes through the optic axes, there is a black cross symmetrically placed on the color pattern, with one arm passing through the centers of both ring systems and the other midway between them (Fig. 81b); but as the polarizers are rotated (while kept crossed), the black cross divides at the center into two right-angle pieces, each of which then rotates about the center of its own color ring system and gradually changes shape; the two finish up as a symmetrical pair of hyperbolic-shaped bands as in Fig. 81c; the system of color rings remains unchanged during this performance. The whole pattern is again a colorful summarized demonstration of the whole optical scheme in a biaxial crystal.

These colored convergent light patterns are not only attractive to look at; they are of great value in the study of crystals, and they are much used by crystallographers and mineralogists in identifying crystals and in studying the complex relations between the optical characteristics and the symmetry of crystals; all good polarizing microscopes are provided with means for observing these patterns on this account. Consider identification, to begin with: the type of pattern immediately informs the observer whether he is looking at a uniaxial crystal which must be either tetragonal, hexagonal, or trigonal, or at a biaxial crystal which must be either orthorhombic, monoclinic, or triclinic. If the crystal is biaxial, the distance between the center of the two ring systems depends on the angle between the optic axes, and this can be measured with fair accuracy. The best way is to mount the preparation on a "universal stage"—a mechanism for tilting in any desired direction—and find the angle through which the crystal has to be tilted to bring first one optic axis and then the other to the center of the field of view. The number of degrees between the optic axes may lead to the identification of the crystal, or at any rate it will narrow down the number of "possibilities" to a very few. Then there are various tricks which have been devised, to find out (by inserting other crystal plates or wedges into the optical system and watching the effect on the color pattern) whether the crystal is positively or negatively birefringent. If the thickness of the crystal is known (and mineralogists do a good deal with rock sections whose thickness can be measured), the number of colored rings which can be seen in the field of view gives a measure of the birefringence of the crystal (difference between the principal refractive indices, i.e., the relative dimensions of the ellipsoidal graph of refractive indices). All these observations together very often lead to positive identification.

Even this is not the end of the story, for some of the crystals of lowest symmetry give color patterns which are abnormal in various ways—by which I mean that they do not conform to the standard description abready given. This is only another illustration of the general rule that the lower the symmetry of a crystal, the more varied are its optical characteristics. In ortho-rhombic crystals—those in which the unit cell is a rectangular brick with unequal edges—symmetry demands (and observation invariably verifies) that the principal axes of the ellipsoid coincide with the unit cell edges. But symmetry has nothing to say about the angle between the optic axes, which is settled by the relative magnitudes between the three refractive indices; now these relative magnitudes need not be the same for different colors (different frequencies) of light, and it may happen that the angle between the optic axes is not the same for red light as it is for blue. If the difference is appreciable, the two black hyperbolas described earlier will not be entirely black, but may have colored edges (Fig. 82a), red outside and violet inside or vice versa (depending on whether the optic axial angle is less for red than for violet or vice versa). An unusually large difference leads, in the mineral brookite (one of the three crystal forms of titanium dioxide), to a convergent whitelight figure which is so riotously

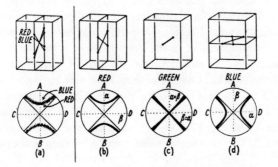

F<small>IG</small>. 82.   The optic axial angle sometimes varies with the color of the light. (a) Convergent light figure for a small difference. (b–d) An extreme variation—brookite, a form of titanium dioxide.

untypical that it is quite unrecognizable as a biaxial figure. To sort out what it means, it is necessary to examine the figure in various colored lights (by putting color filters in the way of the light); and it is then found (Fig. 82b–82d) that the plane of the optic axes for red light is actually at right angles to the plane for blue light. A spectrometer capable of giving monochromatic light of continuously variable frequency gives a most elegant and striking demonstration of the unusual optics of this crystal: as the color is changed from red to yellow, green, blue, and violet, the dark hyperbolas which indicate the magnitude of the optic axial angle gradually come closer together; they merge into a single dark cross for green light, and then open out to a pair of hyperbolas in the plane at right angles to the first as the color changes to blue. Such extremes are rare; but the example illustrates the fascinating versatility of crystals in the tricks they play with light. Is it any wonder that crystallographers and mineralogists sometimes become like collectors of antiques or stamps, and treasure the rarities?

In monoclinic and triclinic crystals the optic axes are still less tied by symmetry. In some circumstances the convergent light figure for red light may be rotated with respect to that for blue light, so that the white light figure looks twisted; in other circumstances it may be unsymmetrical in one way or another; it all depends on which, if any, of the symmetry restrictions still operate. In triclinic crystals none of them operate—the ellipsoidal graph of optical properties may have any orientation whatever with respect to the unit cell, and is free to vary in its orientation as the color changes, in any way whatever, so that the convergent light figure in white light may have no symmetry at all. But in actual fact, large changes with color are rare, and many convergent white light figures of triclinic crystals are quite normal as in Fig. 81c, though they are not often seen central in the field because the ellipsoid is usually inclined to the principal faces.

All the color effects mentioned in this chapter so far are interference effects—they are not in any way due to intrinsic color in crystals any more than the colors of an oil film on a wet road are intrinsic colors. They are all exhibited by quite colorless crystals, and are simply the varied manifestations of the fundamental property of double refraction possessed by all except cubic crystals. The double refraction gives the two rays vibrating in different crystal planes and traveling at different speeds through the crystal, and the polarizers do the rest. But many crystals have, of course, intrinsic colors of their own: some of the minerals used as jewels—rubies and emeralds and sapphires— and many inorganic compounds such as those containing copper or iron, and the organic substances used as dyes or pigments, are strongly colored. What effect has double refraction on these intrinsic colors? You might well ask! The effects are sometimes extremely striking. I am not referring to the modification of the interference effects by intrinsic color, though this of course inevitably occurs. Quite apart from interference effects, the colors of doubly refracting crystals—the colors you see when you simply look through them—exhibit peculiarities which are certainly not shown by colored glass.

Rubies and sapphires, it will be remembered, are colored varieties of corundum (aluminum oxide), which is a crystal of hexagonal symmetry. These stones look distinctly deeper in color when seen along the hexagonal axis than when seen from any direction at right angles to it. This is just one example of a general rule for colored crystals (except cubic ones): the color depends on the direction in which one is looking through the crystal. Often the difference is only one of depth or intensity of color; but for some crystals the color for one viewpoint may be quite different from that seen from a different viewpoint. For instance, some crystals of the mineral cordierite (a magnesium iron aluminosilicate) look dark blue when seen in one direction, light blue in another, and pale yellow in a third direction at right angles to the other two. This seems very odd; the crystal seems to behave as if it were three different substances. However, there is no doubt that the crystal is just one crystal, and if you feel inclined to ask what is the true color of it, the answer is that all three colors are equally true, and that the difference between them is just another example of the great generalization that

crystals have a very fine sense of direction. Just because the
arrangement of atoms in one direction is different from that
in another, all the properties of the crystal vary with direction.
We have seen how the refractive indices vary; and the color
effects are just further examples of the same thing. But to understand these color effects properly and fit them into the general
picture of crystal optics, we shall have to analyze the idea of
intrinsic color more closely, and then see how it fits into the
scheme of ideas which makes a coherent story out of the amazing
facts of double refraction.

In the first place, color in a transparent substance is due to
selective absorption of certain frequencies; white light contains
all the colors of the spectrum, and a piece of red glass looks red
because it absorbs the waves at the blue and green end of the
spectrum, but lets through the red waves; blue glass looks blue
because the blue waves get through while all others are stopped.
Colorless substances are those which do not happen to absorb
any of the frequencies within the range our eyes are capable of
seeing; if our range of perception extended over a wider band
of frequencies, many of the substances which now look transparent and colorless would appear colored or not perfectly
transparent. People who have the misfortune to be color-blind
do not of course experience the glories of color which add so
much to the pleasures of life for the normal color-sensitive
person; presumably the sensations which the color-blind experience are what the color-sensitive person would call various
shades of gray. Color is therefore, first of all, a sensation which
is not the same for all people. Nevertheless, even if we were all
colorblind, instruments like spectrometers would distinguish
between waves of different frequency; and so intrinsic colors are
real in the sense that they denote absorption of waves of certain
frequencies but transmission of other frequencies; or, more
precisely (since absorption is usually partial, not complete), a
greater absorption of some frequencies than of others.

The crystals which appear so different when seen in different
directions therefore absorb only certain wavelengths when the
light is traveling in one direction, but quite different wavelengths

when it is traveling in another direction. But experiments show that it is not really the direction of travel of the light which settles the absorption, but the direction of vibration of the light. This is what we should expect, knowing the facts about double refraction: light is a transverse vibration, and everything that happens in a crystal—the absorption no less than the velocity of light—would be expected to depend on direction of vibration. When we look through a doubly refracting crystal, the light is resolved into two rays polarized at right angles to each other, vibrating in planes prescribed by the crystal structure; and we should expect the absorption as well as the refractive index to depend on the arrangement of atoms in the vibration direction. The two polarized rays therefore would be expected to have different colors, and so the color seen on simply looking through the crystal is a combination of the colors of the two plane-polarized rays.

The individual colors are easily investigated by the use of a polarizer (placed anywhere in the path of the light, either before or after the crystal). In uniaxial crystals it is found that each of the two principal refractive indices is associated with a different color. A ruby, seen from a direction at right angles to the hexagonal axis, looks deep red when the vibration direction of the polarizer is also at right angles to the hexagonal axis (i.e., is transmitting the ordinary ray), but colorless, or nearly so, for light vibrating *along* the hexagonal axis (the extraordinary ray) (Fig. 83); the color seen without the polarizer is the average

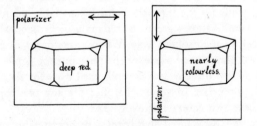

FIG. 83. The color of a ruby depends on the vibration direction of the light.

of the two. We can say therefore that the ordinary ray is deep red while the extraordinary ray is practically colorless. The general name for this phenomenon, where two different colors or shades of color are concerned, is dichroism, and mineralogists sometimes use a simple instrument called a dichroscope, which demonstrates the two colors side by side in a convenient way. A dichroscope is simply a calcite prism in a tube, with a small square aperture at one end. Calcite, as we know, gives a double image, and so, on looking through it, two images of the square aperture, polarized at right angles to each other, are seen side by side. If a dichroic crystal is put over the aperture, correctly oriented, each image is colored differently.

A biaxial crystal has three principal refractive indices, not two, and each of them may be associated with a different color. The mineral andalusite, an aluminum silicate, though colorless when pure, is often colored by the presence of small amounts of other elements, and the colors for the three principal directions in the crystal (the three principal axes of the refractive index ellipsoid) are sometimes quite different; some crystals are yellow for the lowest refractive index, green for the intermediate, and red for the highest. A crystal, viewed in turn from each of the three principal directions, shows always two refractive indices, and thus two colors together—a different pair for each direction. Thus for one direction an andalusite crystal looks greenish yellow, and a dichroscope or a polarizer will show that one ray is green and the other yellow; for a second direction the color is orange, which proves to be a combination of a yellow and a red ray; while for the third the color is inevitably the only other possible combination—green and red in the dichroscope, brownish when seen in the ordinary way. Where three different colors are concerned, the general name for the phenomenon is pleochroism, though the word dichroism is often used even for these crystals —it is appropriate in a way, because for any one aspect of a crystal only two colors are involved.

Although most colored doubly refracting crystals are pleochroic in some degree, really strong pleochroism is rare, and strong pleochroism in contrasting colors still rarer—at least, it is among minerals, the crystals which have been most thoroughly studied from this point of view. I suspect that among the colored organic substances used as dyes and pigments, it will turn out to be more common when we know as much about them as we do about minerals; but not many crystals of this type have been studied in any detail. By far the finest example of pleochroism I have come across is a substance of this type, the zinc derivative of 2,2′, 4,4′-tetraphenyl azadipyrromethine (a cumbrous name, but there is no help for it—it has no common name). It is an intensely blue substance, so deeply colored that crystals visible to the naked eye are quite opaque; very small crystals, however, transmit light, and if a group of them is seen under the microscope in polarized light, it presents a most colorful spectacle, with such varied colors that it is difficult to believe that all the crystals are the same substance. They undoubtedly are, however; and the varied colors simply arise from differences of orientation of the crystals. Parallelogram-shaped crystals (Fig. 84) are ruby

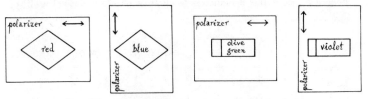

Fig. 84.   A spectacular example of pleochroism.

red in light vibrating along the long diagonal of the parallelogram, and sapphire blue (slightly greenish) in light vibrating along the short diagonal. Crystals turned on their sides so that they have elongated rectangular outlines are deep violet in light vibrating *across* the crystal (this is the third *principal* direction), and rich olive-green in light vibrating *along* the crystal (this is not a principal direction but an intermediate one). Beautiful color effects of a different type are produced by this same substance if it is melted on a microscope slide and allowed to crystallize rapidly; under these circumstances it grows not as isolated single crystals but as radial aggregates. In polarized light each radial aggregate has alternate sectors of contrasting colors, not sharply marked off but merging into each other; many of the aggregates have alternate blue and red sectors, but others are green-blue and violet (again it depends on the crystal orientation). When the polarizer is rotated, each "wheel" rotates independently, and the spectable of all the multicolored wheels rotating rivals any firework display.

Not all pleochroic crystals are colored; in some the different vibration directions are characterised by different degrees of uniform absorption over the whole visible range—in other words, a crystal may appear opaque or gray for one vibration direction, and clear, or, at any rate, a lighter gray, for another. The best-known of such crystals, or rather the one which has been known for the longest time, is the mineral tourmaline, a boroaluminosilicate of very complex and very variable composition; some crystals are black or gray prisms, and examination with a polarizer shows that in light vibrating at right angles to the prism axis the crystal is quite black, while in light vibrating *along* the prism axis it is nearly as clear as window glass (Fig. 85).

FIG. 85.   Dichroism in tourmaline. Two crystals crossed, as in the right-hand sketch, stop light completely.

A slice of such a crystal, cut parallel to the prism axis, can be used as a polarizer; for if ordinary unpolarized light falls on the slice it is resolved in the usual way into two rays polarized at right angles to each other, one along and the other across the prism; but the one across the prism is completely (or almost completely) absorbed, so that the only light getting through is that which vibrates *along* the prism. A pair of such tourmaline plates can be used as crossed polarizers for all the various purposes which have already been mentioned; and indeed in earlier times they were often used instead of Nicol prisms. (Tourmaline is not always black or gray; many crystals are colored, and the color is extremely variable, owing to the variation of the chemical composition: some crystals are green, some red, and some even vary in color from one end to the other—one end may be red and the other green, or there may be several bands of alternating green and red. The dark ones—black, brown, or indigo—are also variable: a crystal may be quite clear and colorless at one end and black at the other. Presumably all such variations are due to changes of chemical composition along the length of the crystal.)

Another crystal showing black-and-white pleochroism is a compound of strychnine sulfate and iodine, sometimes known as herapathite. Attempts to grow sufficiently large crystals to make polarizers were not successful, but a very successful polarizing sheet based on this substance was made in the thirties of the present century. This material, known as "Polaroid," contained tiny crystals of herapathite, all oriented in the same way, embedded in a plastic sheet; although not quite such a perfect polarizer as a Nicol prism, such sheet has the great advantage that it is available in comparatively large areas (compared with a Nicol prism); and owing to its cheapness, it has replaced Nicol prisms in the simpler types of polarizing microscopes. More recently, it has been found possible to make polarizing sheet in other ways; a sheet of polyvinyl alcohol with all the long chain molecules parallel to each other, in which iodine is incorporated, is an exceedingly effective polarizer.

The availability of polarizing sheet at a reasonable price has already led to various applications, and it seems likely that polarized light will play an increasing part in ordinary life. One simple application is in photography: in street scenes, the reflections from shop windows or wet roads which are sometimes troublesome are usually highly polarized, and so it is a simple matter to eliminate them by putting a polarizing sheet, suitably oriented, in front of the camera lens. One system of three-dimensional cinematography is based on the use of polarized light: two stereoscopic images, polarized at right angles to each other, are thrown on the screen, and the spectator wears Polaroid spectacles in which the polarizing sheets are differently oriented so that each eye sees only one of the images; in this way a convincing stereoscopic effect is produced. There are also useful applications to motoring; the confusing reflections from wet roads are strongly polarized, and could be easily eliminated, or very much dimmed, by polarizing sheet on the windscreen; and glare from approaching headlights could be eliminated if both headlights and windscreens were fitted with polarizing sheets suitably oriented: if the light from headlights were vibrating in one plane, and a polarizing sheet on the windscreen had its vibration direction at right angles to this, the light would be eliminated; any intermediate degree of dimming could easily be arranged.

It is curious that the polarization of light, which is of absolutely first-rate importance for understanding the nature of light, does not manifest itself, or obtrude itself on our notice, in ordinary life. This does not mean that natural sources of light are all unpolarized. As a matter of fact, there is plenty of polarized light about, the light from a blue sky (though not from a cloudy one) being partially polarized—the scattering of light sideways by air, which is responsible for the blue color, also leads to polarization; the reason why the polarization is not evident is that there are no natural detectors about. And so polarized light, when we first learn about it, is an oddity, a curiosity. The situation is similar for another fundamental phenomenon—electricity; it too was regarded as a curiosity, something outside the normal run of things, when it was first discovered, and yet we know now that all matter is fundamentally electrical in character. It all goes to show that the really fundamental things are not always the obvious things, and that the keys to the understanding of nature are not, so to speak, handed to us on a plate. To make any progress in understanding we have to be prepared to investigate patiently by experiment.

It is the same with ideas, whether in science or in any other subject: the ideas which come into our minds spontaneously— the intuitions or hunches that all of us get sometimes—are not necessarily correct, or even if more or less correct, not necessarily the most important or significant aspects of the subject in question. You might think that, just because we are embedded in our environment like a fish in water, just because we have evolved in it and are more or less adapted to it, the phenomena that present themselves to our senses and the ideas that come into our heads would naturally correspond to the essential features of that environment. But, as we know, it is not always so; many phenomena, taken superficially, are misleading, or do not reveal the essentials, and many false ideas have come into people's heads and, accepted uncritically, have stood in the way of progress in knowledge or behavior. This is not to decry the value of intuitions, either in science or in any other subject: they have played a very important part in scientific discovery as well as in the development of ideas on morals and religion. But how do we distinguish between true and false intuitions? Or, to use a more cautious and more valid phrase, how do we distinguish between an intuition which is fruitful and capable of leading on to a wider conceptual linkup between varied phenomena and one which is barren and contains within it hidden self-contradictions? Only by testing it in an unprejudiced spirit against a wider and wider array of facts, and by patient experiment to uncover, in all humility, many more phenomena in addition to the ones under our noses. This outlook is, of course, thoroughly accepted in science—it is the very foundation of science, which is only another name for the application of intellect and honesty to the understanding of the material world. But is it yet sufficiently accepted in other subjects of inquiry? Faraday had an intuition that all the forms of energy —heat, electricity, magnetism, light—were closely interrelated and interconvertible; but he was not content, as many philosophers have been, to talk about the idea and behave as if it were true just because it came into his head; he spent his life testing it, looking for evidence by whatever experiments he could devise, and being willing to be proved wrong if the evidence pointed that way. Can it be said that the well-known figures who have made pronouncements in politics or economics or ethics or religion have been equally honest or equal in humility?

CHAPTER 11

Through the Looking Glass

Highly symmetrical crystals are all very well in their way; their perfection commands respect and perhaps admiration, and at those times when we feel in a "classical" mood, when undeviating perfection of form seems the highest aesthetic pinnacle, we may well be content to approve ungrudgingly their pride of place in the hierarchy of the crystal kingdom. But in less austere moods, is there not, in those cubic crystals which possess all the possible symmetries, a certain smugness, an air of self-satisfaction which comes from possessing all the virtues, a certain dullness born of exact repetition in all three dimensions? Certainly a crystal with the shape of a perfect cube is easily appreciated formally, and soon there is nothing left to contemplate, unless we find in the internal atomic pattern some intricacies which absorb our attention in the effort to see how the details build up the perfection of the whole. Crystals of the highest symmetry which grow in shapes with many facets may likewise attract something more than respect; the very profusion of faces does something to mitigate the austere impression created by the perfection of the symmetry—like baroque ornamentation on a classic background.

From such an excess of perfection, it is sometimes a relief to turn to lesser symmetries. Some of the hexagonal and tetragonal crystals have more character, and on that account are more attractive to look at and to contemplate. In their shape and in their structure, they are more interesting than the cubic crystals: the difference between the one direction of hexagonal or tetragonal symmetry and the other direction gives a certain amount of variety. Tetragonal or hexagonal prisms having the highest symmetry possible in each of these systems seem to have an aristocratic air—an impression produced perhaps by the dominance of the unique axis, coupled with the high symmetry about that axis (see Fig. 86). Further down in the symmetry scale, the crystals with alternating axes, like urea and calcite, have a more individual character, while in the polar classes—those in which one end of the tetragonal or hexagonal axis is developed differently from the other—character is carried to the pitch of eccentricity.

With the orthorhombic system we come to a more democratic regime: all three directions are different, but none is favored (at any rate in the highest symmetry class), and yet the combination has an air of solid respectability based on the sound rectangular framework. Nevertheless, there is a place in democratic society for eccentrics, provided that they keep to the fundamental rectangular framework, and this is found in the polar class of the orthorhombic system, where one axis is differently developed at the two ends.

The monoclinic system begins to break away from rectangular respectability; but the deviation is restrained, and the moderately skew character, though it may give a rakish impression, is on the whole a romantic trait. For sheer bohemianism you have to go to the triclinic system, where all restraints (apart from the straight-line character which is the foundation of the crystal kingdom) are abandoned, and the structure is rakish in all directions. It is somehow appropriate that the "romantic" monoclinic system is the center of gravity of the crystal kingdom in the sense that more substances crystallize in monoclinic structures than in any others.

Having said all this, I must now admit that there are some crystals which do not seem to me to fit into any of my categories: they seem to stand apart from the rest. Examples occur in all the systems; everywhere throughout the crystal kingdom there are individuals which in some respects are so different from the rest that they seem to require a separate treatment and a special name. Since they occur in all systems, they cut right across the general scheme. I am referring to those crystals which have no planes of symmetry and no center of symmetry—those which lack the elements of symmetry which convert any morphological or structural feature into its mirror image. Owing to this lack,

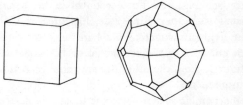

TOO PERFECT ?   *Aristocratic*

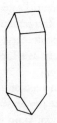 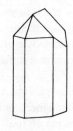 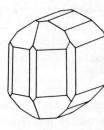 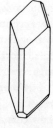

More
Character ?   *Eccentric*   Solid Respectability   *Romantic*

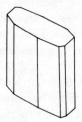 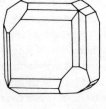 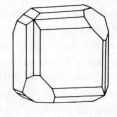

Rakish   THE MYSTICS

Crystal Characters.

FIG. 86. Crystal characters.

a crystal of this type is not identical with its mirror image; in fact, for all such substances it is possible to obtain two kinds of crystals which differ in that one is the nonidentical mirror image of the other. In other respects they are identical—they are the same in chemical composition and in density, they are composed of the same atoms linked in the same way, and they have unit cells of the same shape and size; but the crystals differ in the way that a left hand differs from a right hand. An example has already been given in Fig. 35 (sodium chlorate); just as a left-hand glove cannot be worn on a right hand, so a ghost of a left-hand sodium chlorate crystal could not fit on to a right-hand crystal of the same substance. I would not call such crystals eccentrics, for they have a significance in crystallography and in other ways which entitles them to a more serious and dignified title; they have some optical characteristics which are even more strange than the double refraction which many crystals show, and they played a part in the development of chemistry which, 100 years ago, caught the imagination of the scientific world. They are the mystics of the crystal kingdom.

The first such crystal to attract attention was quartz, the commonest crystal form of silica, and indeed one of the commonest minerals. In the early years of the nineteenth century, Haüy— that same abbé who first explained in a quantitative way the relations between the different faces of crystals—noticed that on many quartz crystals there are small facets so placed that any one crystal is not identical with its mirror image, and that on some crystals the facets are inclined in one direction while on others they are oppositely inclined. In fact the two sorts of quartz crystals are (apart from accidental inequalities in the sizes of the various faces) mirror images of each other, but not identical. They are illustrated in Fig. 87; the facets in question are those marked x, y, and z; and if we call the one on the left a left-handed crystal, the other is right-handed. Facets which give a crystal a lower symmetry than it would have without them are called hemihedral, meaning a half-set of facets; and crystal shapes which are nonidentical mirror images of each other are called "enantiomorphic forms" or "enantiomorphs."

At about the same time—in 1811, to be precise—D. F. J. Arago and J. B. Biot were studying, in Paris, the optical properties of quartz, and noticed some unusual features. Quartz belongs to the hexagonal system, and would be expected to have optical characteristics like those of calcite, in which the hexagonal axis is the one direction of single refraction, so that if one looks straight down the hexagonal axis when the crystal is between crossed polarizers, the crystal shows no interference colors, but is dark, and stays dark when the crossed polarizers (or the crystal) are rotated. But if one looks down the hexagonal axis of a quartz crystal which is between crossed polarizers (a slice cut perpendicular to the hexagonal axis is necessary, to avoid disturbing refraction effects), the crystal is not dark but colored, and rotation of the polarizers does not bring about extinction or indeed any change at all in the appearance; it is evidently

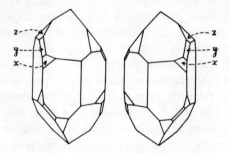

FIG. 87.   Left- and right-handed quartz crystals, with hemihedral facets x, y, and z.

not a case of ordinary double refraction. The color depends on the thickness of the crystal plate; and if instead of rotating both polarizers together one rotates only the upper one (often called the analyzer), a whole series of color changes occurs. A plate 1 millimeter thick looks, between crossed polarizers, a bluish white, but on rotating the analyzer in one particular direction the color changes successively to greenish blue, purplish red, orange, and yellow. The explanation of these color changes was found by using for illumination various colored lights in turn:

if red monochromatic light is used, crossed polarizers let a little of it through, but rotation of the analyzer 15° in one particular direction produces extinction; for yellow light (the next in the spectrum order) 21° rotation in the same direction is necessary for extinction; while for green light 27° rotation is required; and for blue light 33° rotation is necessary. Evidently the quartz crystal rotates the plane of polarization by an amount which depends on the frequency of the light: the higher frequency blue light is rotated over twice as much as the lower frequency red light. Further experiments with quartz plates of different thicknesses showed that the amount of rotation for any particular color of light is exactly proportional to the thickness; evidently something in the crystal rotates the plane of polarization progressively as the light goes through the crystal; and, most significantly, the rotation is in one direction in some quartz crystals and in the opposite direction in others.

With this knowledge the explanation of the color effects in white light is straightforward: for a plate 1 millimeter thick, rotation of the analyzer by 15° has the effect of extinguishing red light, but the other colors of the spectrum are still there in varying degrees, combining in the eye to produce the complementary color greenish blue; a further rotation to 21° extinguishes yellow light, leaving the complementary blue; while 27° extinguishes green, leaving the complementary purplish red.

Arago and Biot do not seem to have connected these unusual optical effects with the facets noticed by Haüy; but soon afterwards (in 1820) it was definitely suggested by the English astronomer Sir John Herschel that the two are intimately connected, for it was found that crystals which are morphologically left-handed rotate in one direction, while right-handed crystals rotate in the opposite direction. A further step (made by Fresnel in 1827) was to suppose that there is something of a helical nature in the structure of the crystal which is responsible both for the rotation of the plane of polarization and for the little asymmetric facets. This idea seemed to be strongly supported by an ingenious experiment by Reusch, who piled a number of thin mica plates in a helical fashion and found that this arrangement gives a convincing imitation of the rotation effect in quartz—the more convincing, the thinner the plates and the greater the number. We know now, as the result of the study of the atomic arrangement in quartz by X-ray diffraction methods, that there is indeed a helical arrangement of atoms in the structure, like a left-handed screw in some crystals and a right-handed screw in others. (But do not suppose that the plane of polarization of the light rotates in step with the atomic corkscrews in quartz; it is not so. The fact is that the atomic corkscrews merely provide *something* which is capable of twisting the vibration plane of the light a little; each turn of the atomic corkscrew twists the plane only a very minute amount, and millions of them are required to build up a twist of a few degrees.)

Still more surprising was Biot's discovery (1815–1820) that certain liquids and solutions—oil of turpentine, and solutions of sugar and tartaric acid—actually do the same thing as quartz crystals, and twist the vibration plane of polarized light. A crystal is a precisely ordered structure with all sorts of directional properties, but in a liquid or a solution, the molecules are oriented in a quite random manner. How can such a chaotic structure produce this very special directional effect of rotation of the vibration plane of light? We can begin to understand it with the help of the corkscrew idea, for the great thing about a screw is that if it is right-handed when seen from one end, it is just as right-handed when seen from the other end or from any other direction. If molecules of turpentine and sugar and tartaric acid are screwlike, we can compare any one of these liquids to a bucket of right-handed screws; the jumble of screws, even though they are pointing in all directions, undoubtedly has a general right-handed character, and in the same way a liquid, if it consists entirely of right-handed screwlike molecules, has a general right-handed character. If any one molecule rotates the vibration plane of light to the right, then the jumble of molecules as a whole will do the same thing. In the early years of the nineteenth century when these optical rotation effects were discovered, the shapes of these molecules were unknown. As a matter of fact the shapes, now that we do know them, are not really like corkscrews, but the screw picture is sound in principle, and will do for a start. We will return to the actual shapes later on.

The amount of rotation of the vibration plane of any particular color of light in turpentine depends on the thickness of turpentine through which the light travels. For a solution of sugar the amount of rotation depends on the amount of sugar in the path of the light—that is, on the strength of the solution and the thickness through which the light passes. This seems natural enough, and corresponds to what happens in quartz crystals. But in one respect there is a striking difference between the rotating liquids and quartz crystals: some quartz crystals rotate to the left and others rotate by a precisely equal amount to the right, but *all* oil of turpentine rotates to the left (counterclockwise if one looks towards the light) and *all* cane sugar to the right. Moreover, all the rotating liquids found in nature come from living plants or animals—they are animal or vegetable, not mineral. One naturally asks, is there any connection between the one-direction rotation and the special chemistry of living things?

At this point Pasteur steps into the story. It was his discoveries in this field that first made him famous, and his experiences in this work helped to direct his inquiring mind toward the fundamental phenomena in the chemistry of living things which were to be the main interests of his career. It all started in this way. In the forties of last century the scientific world—or at any rate that part of it which was interested in crystals and polarized light—was puzzled and baffled by some of the facts which had turned up about tartaric acid, the acid in grape juice which crystallizes out in wine vats. It had been known since 1820 that a solution of ordinary tartaric acid rotates the vibration plane of polarized light to the left (counterclockwise as one looks toward the light). But occasionally—and notably in one particular wine factory—crystals of tartaric acid appeared which had no effect whatever on polarized light, although they seemed in all other respects just the same as the normal crystals; these unusual crystals were called paratartaric acid or racemic acid (from *racemus*, grape), but the former name is now obsolete, so we shall use only the latter. The German crystallographer, E.

Mitscherlich, and the French crystallographer, M. de la Provostaye, had both made extensive studies of the two tartaric acids and their salts, and both reported that the two acids have the same chemical composition, the same crystal shape, the same angles, the same density, the same double refraction, and the same angles between the optic axes; their solutions have the same refractive index, *but* the solution of the ordinary tartaric acid rotates the plane of polarization while the solution of racemic acid is entirely inactive in this way. And the same was said to be true for all the salts of the two acids.

This was all very disconcerting. It did not fit in with experience with other substances, for usually substances with so many properties precisely equal were identical in all respects. It made rotation of the plane of polarized light seem more mysterious than even; and it produced in the minds of those who thought about it those gnawing doubts which are so often the focal points of new discoveries.

Pasteur had only just graduated. He was fascinated by this problem, and resolved to study these crystals and try to clear up the mystery. But let him tell the story in his own words: "I meditated for a long time on Mitscherlich's note; it disturbed my schoolboy thoughts. I could not understand that two substances could be as similar as claimed by Mitscherlich without being completely identical. To know how to wonder and question is the first step of the mind towards discovery. Hardly graduated from the École Normale, I planned to prepare a long series of crystals, with the purpose of studying their shapes. The crystals of tartaric and racemic acids and their salts are as beautiful as they are easy to prepare; and I could constantly control the accuracy of my determinations by referring to the memoir of an able and precise physicist, M. de la Provostaye, who had published an extensive crystallographic study of tartaric and racemic acids and their salts. I soon recognized that tartaric acid and its salts exhibit dissymetric forms; the mirror image of each of these crystals was not superposable upon the crystal itself. On the other hand, I could not find anything of the sort in racemic acid or its salts."

This was the first discovery, which his predecessors had missed: crystals of tartaric acid and its salts have facets which proclaim a lack of the symmetries that convert left-handed to right-handed features (planes of symmetry, or a center of symmetry), and it was natural to suppose that this is connected with the ability of solutions to rotate the plane of polarized light; and that, on the other hand, the absence of the facets from racemic acid and its salts is likewise connected with the fact that their solutions have no effect on polarized light. Pursuing the matter further, Pasteur then turned to the double sodium ammonium salts of the two acids, because Mitscherlich had particularly studied these crystals.

"Immediately, and with a feverish ardor, I prepared the double tartrate of sodium and ammonium, as well as the corresponding racemate, and proceeded to compare the crystal forms, with the preconceived notion that I would find dissymmetry in the tartrate and not in the racemate. Thus, I thought, everything will come clear; the mystery of Mitscherlich's note will be solved, the dissymmetry in the crystal form of the tartrate will correspond to its optical dissymmetry and the absence of dissymmetry in the crystal form of the racemate will correspond to the inability of this salt to deviate the plane of polarized light. And indeed I saw that the crystals of the tartrate of sodium and ammonium exhibited the small facets revealing dissymmetry. But when I turned to examine the crystals of the racemate, for an instant my heart stopped beating: *all the crystals exhibited the facets of dissymmetry!*"

Here was apparently a disappointment: why should the racemate, which does not rotate the plane of polarized light, form dissymmetric (hemihedral) crystals? But it was not a disappointment for long: "The fortunate idea came to me to orient the crystals with reference to a plane perpendicular to the observer, and then I noticed that the confused mass of crystals of racemate could be divided into two groups according to the orientation of their facets of dissymmetry. In one group the facet of dissymmetry nearer my body was inclined to the right with reference to the plane of orientation which I have just mentioned, whereas the facet of dissymmetry was inclined to the left in the other. The racemate was in fact a mixture of two kinds of crystals, some dissymmetric to the right, some dissymmetric to the left." The shapes of the crystals are shown in Fig. 88.

"A new and obvious idea soon occurred to me. Those crystals dissymmetric to the right, which I could separate manually from the others, exhibited an absolute identity of shape with those of the classical right tartrate. Pursuing my preconceived idea, in the logic of its deductions, I separated these right crystals from the crystallized racemate; I made the lead salt and isolated the acid; this acid appeared absolutely identical with the tartaric acid of grape, identical also in its action on polarized light. My happiness was even greater on the day when,

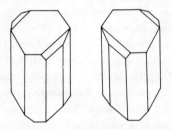

FIG. 88. Left- and right-handed crystals of sodium ammonium tartrate hydrate.

separating now from the racemate the crystals dissymmetric to the left, and making their acid, I obtained a tartaric acid absolutely similar to the tartaric acid of grape but with an opposite dissymmetry, and also with an opposite action on light. Its shape was identical with that of a mirror image of the right tartaric acid, and, other things being equal, it rotated to the left as much in absolute amount as the other acid did to the right. Finally, when I mixed solutions containing equal weights of these two acids, the mixture gave rise to a crystalline mass of racemic acid identical with the known racemic acid." (Both acids pack together in crystals of racemic acid; they do not form separate left and right crystals. Pasteur was lucky in his decision to concentrate on sodium ammonium racemate, which is one of the few substances that do give separate left and right crystals.)

The mystery was solved: racemic acid is just a mixture of two acids, similar except for their opposite action on polarized light, one of them being completely identical with ordinary tartaric acid, and the other presumably its mirror image. Evidently molecules, like crystals, can have left- and right-handed forms. This discovery had a profound effect on people's ideas about molecules, and started lively speculations on their shapes and symmetries which played an important part in the development of organic chemistry, the chemistry of the carbon compounds of which living tissues are composed. There must have been many people in those days (and indeed for long afterward) who hardly dared to believe that the atoms and molecules which the chemist talked about really existed; they thought of them as convenient ideas—as mental scaffolding on which to erect theories—but not necessarily as having any real existence. The reality might be something nebulous and beyond our comprehension, something which produced all the phenomena which made chemists have illusions to which they gave the names atoms and molecules. But the discovery of the left- and right-handed tartaric acids helped to bring molecules out of the mist into the very concrete world of geometry.

Crystals of the two mirror-image tartaric acids rotate the plane of polarized light, just as quartz crystals do; and they rotate it in opposite directions by the same amount. [In birefringent crystals, rotation can be observed conveniently only by looking directly along an optic axis (a direction of single refraction); the tartaric acids, being monoclinic, are optically biaxial, and in order to observe and measure the rotation it is necessary to cut plates perpendicular to either of the optic axes.] But there is one very important difference between the two tartaric acids and the two kinds of quartz crystals. If one of the tartaric acids is dissolved or melted, the liquid also rotates the plane of polarization, and likewise, if melted tartaric acid is cooled quickly so that it solidifies to a glass, the glass also rotates; but if any quartz crystal is melted or dissolved, the solution or the glass has no effect whatever on polarized light. The reason is that the molecules of quartz are not themselves screwlike—it is only the arrangement of them in the crystal that is screwlike, so that as soon as the arrangement is destroyed, all possibility of rotation vanishes. In tartaric acid, on the other hand, it is the molecules themselves that are primarily responsible for the rotation: the arrangement in the crystal modifies the rotation, but it is the arrangement of the atoms in the molecule that is responsible for the rotation in the liquid or glass state.

The molecules of tartaric acid are, as we know now, not really screwlike. Indeed, Pasteur, even in 1850, realized that they need not actually have a screwlike shape: a molecule might be able to rotate the plane of polarized light provided only that it has a form which is not identical with its mirror image—and a screw is not the only form of this sort. Observe the shapes of the crystals shown in Fig. 88; each crystal is not identical with its mirror image, yet the shapes are not like screws. The molecules might be of the same type—not, of course, the same shape as the crystals, but a shape having the same lack of symmetry. The word "asymmetric" is often used in referring to such shapes, but it is not the most appropriate word, and may be misleading because its literal meaning is "without symmetry"—that is, without symmetry of any sort. Molecules or crystals which are not identical with their mirror images need not be entirely without symmetry—witness the crystals of the tartaric acids themselves, which have axes of twofold symmetry, and those of quartz which have axes of sixfold symmetry. What is essential is that they shall lack planes of symmetry or a center of symmetry—the elements which convert any morphological feature into its mirror image; they may possess axes of symmetry, as both tartaric acid crystals and quartz crystals do. The correct word for this sort of thing is "enantiomorphism." Pasteur's word "dissymmetry" is better than "asymmetry"; after a period of neglect, it is now coming back into use.

Pasteur gave a graphic account of the difference between tartaric acid and quartz in a lecture he gave in 1860. "Are the atoms in the dextro ("right-rotating") acid grouped in the form of a right-handed spiral, or are they placed at the apex of an irregular tetrahedron, or are they disposed according to this or that dissymmetric arrangement? We do not know. Quartz, you will say at once, possesses the two characteristics of dissymmetry—the hemihedry in form ('half-set of faces') observed by Haüy and the optical activity discovered by Arago and Biot! Nevertheless, molecular dissymmetry is entirely absent in quartz. To understand this, let us take a further step in the knowledge of the phenomena with which we are dealing. Permit me to illustrate roughly, but with essential accuracy, the structure of quartz and the natural organic products. Imagine a spiral stairway whose steps are cubes or any other objects with superposable mirror images. Destroy the structure of the stairway and the dissymmetry will have vanished. The dissymmetry of the stairway was simply the result of the mode of arrangement of the component steps. Such is quartz. The crystal of quartz is the stairway complete. It is hemihedral; it acts on polarized light by virtue of this. But let the crystal be dissolved, fused, or have its physical structure destroyed in any way whatever; its dissymmetry is suppressed, and with it all action on polarized light, as it would be, for example, with a solution of alum, a liquid formed of molecules of cubic structure distributed without order. Imagine, on the other hand, the same spiral stairway to be constructed with irregular tetrahedra for steps. Destroy the stairway and the dissymmetry will still exist, since we are dealing with a collection of tetrahedra. They may occupy any positions whatever, yet each of them will nevertheless have dissymmetry of its own. Such are the organic substances in which each molecule has a dissymmetry of its own, revealing itself in crystal form. When the crystal is destroyed by solution, there results a liquid of molecules, without arrangement, it is true, but each having a dissymmetry in the same sense, if not of the same intensity in all directions.

"When the atoms of organic molecules are dissymmetrically arranged, the molecular dissymmetry is betrayed by a crystal form exhibiting nonsuperposable hemihedrism. The presence of molecular dissymmetry reveals itself by optical activity. When this nonsuperposable molecular dissymmetry appears in two forms, as in the dextro and laevo ('right and left') tartaric acids and all their derivatives, then the chemical properties of the identical but opposite substances are exactly the same, from which it follows that this type of contrast and analogy does not interfere with the ordinary play of the chemical affinities."

The waves of discovery which spread outward from Pasteur's achievement are extremely varied, but we shall consider only two of the most important. Both of them are concerned with the question of the types of molecules which are "optically active"—that is, have the ability to rotate the plane of polarized light. First, how are the atoms in tartaric acid and other optically active substances linked together, and what are the actual shapes and symmetries of the molecules? And second, what has molecular dissymmetry to do with life?

With the development of organic chemistry, it became clear that a carbon atom is capable of linking to four other atoms, and it was natural to suppose that the four links might be uniformly distributed in space—that is, that the angles between all four links might be equal. Such a distribution in space is known as "tetrahedral" because the links can be thought of as directed from the center of a regular tetrahedron toward its four corners (Fig. 89). The Dutchman Van 't Hoff and the Frenchman Le Bel realized independently and simultaneously (in 1874) that a molecule consisting of a central carbon atom linked to four quite different atoms or groups would have no symmetry whatever, and would be capable of optical activity, provided that the

Fig. 89. A carbon atom with four links to other atoms, tetrahedrally disposed. When the four other atoms or groups of atoms are all different, the arrangement has no symmetry.

four links were not in a plane but perhaps tetrahedrally disposed; and sufficient information about optically active substances had then accumulated to show that many of them were indeed of that type. Subsequent experience has confirmed this generalization, and for many types of organic compound, if one wishes to know whether the molecules are capable of optical activity, it is only necessary to look at its formula (the system of atomic links); if it contains one or more "asymmetric carbon atoms"— that is, carbon atoms linked to four *different* atoms or groups— then it is capable of optical activity. Of course it is really the molecular symmetry, or rather dissymmetry, that counts, and there are some types of molecule which do not have "asymmetric carbon atoms," but which nevertheless are enantiomorphous and are therefore capable of optical activity; nevertheless, whenever a molecule has one four-linked carbon atom linked to four *different* atoms or groups, the molecule necessarily has an enantiomorphic character so that optical activity is certain. One of the simplest optically active substances is malic acid, the acid of apples; its formula is

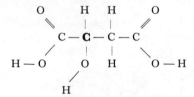

and it contains one asymmetric carbon atom (the one in heavy type).

Tartaric acid is a slightly more complicated molecule; its scheme of chemical linkages is

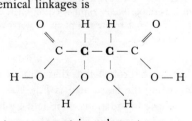

so it contains two asymmetric carbon atoms.

In the present century the study of the scattering of X-rays by crystals has enabled us to find the precise positions of atoms —the arrangement of them, their exact distances apart, and the angles between the links. The results of such studies of many different substances have shown that the four links of a carbon are indeed tetrahedrally arranged; and the molecules of the two tartaric acids have the shapes shown in Figs. 90a and 90b. But until 1950, one piece of information was still missing: Beevers and Hughes found, by straightforward methods, that ordinary dextro or right-rotating tartaric acid has either the configuration shown in Fig. 90a or the mirror image configuration Fig. 90b, but it was still not known which is correct, because the X-ray diffraction patterns of the two mirror-image forms of Rochelle salt are, under ordinary conditions, precisely the same. Eventually, Bijvoet, working appropriately enough in the Van 't Hoff laboratory in Utrecht, devised an ingenious method

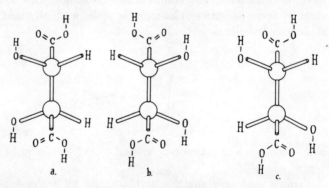

FIG. 90. (a) The left- and (b) right-rotating forms of tartaric acid. [It is now known that the ordinary right-rotating form is (b).] (c) Meso-tartaric acid, which does not rotate the plane of polarized light because it has a center of symmetry.

which led at last to the knowledge that natural dextro tartaric acid is Fig. 90b, while the laevo acid is Fig. 90a. The edifice of stereochemistry whose foundations were laid by Pasteur is now, as far as tartaric acid is concerned, complete.

The existence in the tartaric acid molecule of two asymmetric carbon atoms has one other interesting consequence. The molecule is in two halves, identical with each other chemically, and in ordinary right-rotating tartaric acid each half is right-rotating; the total rotation is a combination of the separate rotations of the two identical halves. Similarly, the other (laevo or left-rotating) tartaric acid consists of two left-rotating halves, each of them mirror images of a right-rotating half of the dextro acid. But what happens if a left-rotating half is joined to a right-rotating half? As you might expect, the molecule does not rotate the plane of polarized light at all, it is a third different tartaric acid. This third form, known as mesotartaric acid, was discovered by Pasteur, who made it by heating a solution of the cinchonine salt of ordinary tartaric acid; it has different properties from left or right tartaric acids or racemic acid—a different density and a different melting point—and it cannot be separated into left and right components by any of the methods which Pasteur discovered for racemic components, naturally, because it is an inherently symmetric, optically inactive molecule (Fig. 90c). Many other molecules are now known which have more than two asymmetric carbon atoms (the sugars are important examples); and the number of different types of molecule grows rapidly with the number of asymmetric carbon atoms.

These facts are of great importance for the science of stereo-chemistry—the science of the arrangement of atoms in space. But the most fascinating and momentous question which Pasteur asked, and which we all ask as soon as we know the facts about optically active substances, is, "What has molecular dissymmetry to do with life?" All the substances found in nature which are optically active in solution or liquid form come from plants or animals; those of mineral origin, and all substances made in the laboratory by ordinary chemical methods from minerals, or indeed from any inactive substances, are not optically active in solution or liquid form. These facts suggested at first (and Pasteur clung to this view) that enantiomorphous molecules are produced only in living things, and that an asymmetric character of some sort is a fundamental characteristic of living matter. But it was soon shown that substances like racemic acid can be synthesized in the laboratory; so it is at any rate possible to synthesize both left- and right-handed molecules simultaneously in equal numbers. What is not possible by ordinary chemical methods is to produce one without the other. The reason is easy to see; when molecules are made by joining atoms together, the chances of the atoms joining to make a left-handed molecule are precisely the same as for a right-handed molecule, so that any attempt to make a substance whose molecules contain an asymmetric carbon atom must result in the formation of a racemic mixture containing equal numbers of left and right molecules.

How is it, then, that living plants and animals *are* able to produce one without the other? One way in which this comes about (though this is not an explanation, it only transfers the mystery to the distant past) is by producing one type of enantio-morphous molecule from a chemically different but also enantio-morphous molecule which is already present in the living organism—for this is always possible, even in the laboratory, provided that the essential asymmetric grouping of atoms is not disturbed (but only another part of the molecule). But the already present substance was in turn produced from another, and so on, back through myriads of generations of living creatures, back to the beginnings of the species in which the substance is found, back further through the slow processes of evolution, and so to the very beginning of life on earth. Another type of chemical process which plays an important part in establishing one type of enantiomorphous molecule rather than its mirror image is that which is at the bottom of one of the methods of separating enantiomorphs discovered by Pasteur. He found that when a solution of ammonium racemate is fermented by a particular mold, it becomes left-rotating, and as soon as the rotation ceases to increase, the fermentation stops; evidently the mold consumes or destroys the right-rotating molecules and leaves the left-rotating ones untouched. In this way a solution of racemate, which contains equal numbers of both sorts of molecule and is optically inactive, is converted into a solution of left-rotating tartrate. This sort of thing must be happening continuously in living organisms, so that even when a chemical reaction produces equal numbers of left and right molecules, one type is destroyed by one of the organs of the living creature itself or by one of the other organisms which are present in it.

In either case the origin of the existence of one-handed molecules has to be traced back to the early history of living creatures, probably to the very beginning of life on earth—for the one-handedness of substances in living creatures is not confined to by-products, but is an essential feature of the all-important substances like proteins, which are the very basis of living tissues. When the first living matter appeared, something made the essential substances right-handed,* and they have stayed right-handed, so that we and all living creatures are irrevocable committed to a chemically right-handed existence. The extent to which this is true is shown by some very striking facts about the chemical structure of proteins. These substances are composed of giant molecules made up of many asymmetric atomic groups, called amino acid residues, strung together. There are about twenty different types of amino acid residues used in this way, and all the proteins, from different parts of the same animal, and from all the different species of animals, are made up of different combinations of selections of these twenty, strung together in different proportions and probably in different orders. It is an astounding fact that all the amino acid residues in all the proteins are all asymmetric in the same sense—the asymmetric carbon atom in them is joined to four different groups in such a way that chemically corresponding groups are always in corresponding positions in space. Such uniformity can hardly be accidental, and suggests a common origin for all the chemical building units of protein molecules.

The origin of life was evidently bound up with an original asymmetric chemical synthesis. At some time millions of years ago, and perhaps at .one place on the earth, or, more precisely,

---

* I call these substances right-handed because protein molecules curl up into the form of a right-handed screw. See Chapter 14.

in the shallow coastal waters at some favored spot, right-handed molecules and not left-handed ones were made. There has naturally been a great deal of speculation on how this happened. One possibility is that it happened on a particular quartz crystal: an asymmetric arrangement of atoms on its surface acted as a template on which an asymmetric amino acid was formed. There is, of course, an objection to this: there are plenty of quartz crystals of both types about, and if right-handed molecules can be formed on one type, left-handed molecules are equally likely to be formed on the other type. This objection might be met by assuming that a rare combination of chemical conditions was necessary, and happened only near one crystal. And if it is further objected that even a rare combination might be repeated subsequently near a crystal of opposite type (and might in fact be happening occasionally all the time), this objection also might be met by the argument that a right-handed sequence of chemical syntheses, once established and gaining momentum in the development of more complex types, might dominate the situation and lead to the destruction of subsequently formed left-handed molecules.

Another possibility is that the first asymmetric synthesis happened as a result of a particular effect of light on a chemical reaction. Some chemical reactions are accelerated by visible light, and others will not go at all without it. But ordinary unpolarized light would not be expected to influence the strictly impartial course of a reaction which normally produces equal numbers of left and right molecules; nor would plane polarized light: there is a certain amount of plane polarized light in the light from a blue sky, but there is nothing asymmetric about plane polarized light, and so the existence of it does not help to explain asymmetric synthesis. But we have not yet exhausted all the subtleties of polarized light, and as a matter of fact it is possible to have a beam of light whose vibrations do give it a screwlike, asymmetric character: the vibrations are not in a plane, but are circular or elliptical, and this, coupled with the onward travel of the light waves, means asymmetry in the beam. Circularly and elliptically polarized beams are not uncommon. If plane polarized light is sent through a birefringent crystal in the 45° position, it comes out as two components, plane-polarized at right angles, one retarded behind the other. If one of the components is a quarter of a wavelength behind the other, any particle which experiences the vibrations of both components will find itself moving in a circle; if the lag is three-quarters of a wavelength, again the motion is circular but in the opposite direction; but if the lag is of any other magnitude (apart from a whole or a half wavelength), the motion is elliptical. Circular polarization is also found in light which has come through a quartz crystal; the rotation of the plane of polarization which I have already described in a simple way has been found to be the resultant of a more elaborate process. Actually there are two circularly polarized beams rotating in opposite directions and traveling at slightly different speeds (they can be separated, though with difficulty). But, most significant of all for the problem of asymmetric synthesis, it has been found that the light reflected by the sea is always to some extent elliptically polarized, and contains an excess of light rotating in one particular direction. Why this should be is not known; it might be due to the magnetic field of the earth (which is associated with its rotation); but it is a fact, and this asymmetry of the light in just the place where life probably started is highly suggestive.

Can circularly or elliptically polarized light influence chemical reactions in the way envisaged, and create one-handed molecules only, or at any rate a preponderance of one sort? Quite recently, in the thirties of the present century, it has been found that circularly polarized light can do this; the asymmetric molecules made in this way were not the sort which may have been the raw materials for the development of living matter, but it is something to have shown that this sort of effect of light on a chemical reaction is possible at all.

These are only hints, of course; we have a long way to go before we can say we have a plausible idea of how life started. Quite apart from the asymmetry of the molecules, the chemistry of the formation of such substances as proteins is only dimly understood. But if, as Pasteur believed, molecular asymmetry is an essential characteristic of the chemistry of life (not merely an accidental feature added on), then the origin of asymmetric molecules in nature is one of the most important questions in science, and is worthy of all the efforts chemists can put into it. Meanwhile, we speculate. Some people favor the view that one singular event, like the clinging of simple molecules to a face of a quartz crystal and their linking together to form an asymmetric prototype of a protein molecule, started off the chain of life-chemistry. Pasteur thought that some general feature of the environment, possibly connected with the rotation of the earth, might be responsible—an idea which may have some connection with the elliptical polarization of light reflected by the sea; and it must be said that a broad general feature seems more appropriate as the instigator of such a momentous chain of events than a rare localized incident. But we do not know.

CHAPTER 12

Patterns in Space

If you wanted to design a repeating pattern for a wallpaper or a dress material, how would you go about it? Would you draw a motif first, and then draw exactly similar repetitions around it (perhaps linking them up in some way), and continue the repetition to build up the indefinitely repeating pattern? Or would you lay down a framework first, specifying that the pattern units must be spaced so many inches apart in each direction, and then design the motif to fit onto this predetermined framework? The first method corresponds to what the molecules do when they get together to form a crystal nucleus. A molecule is the motif of the three-dimensional space pattern we call a crystal; its size and shape are already settled, and when a number of them get together (being pulled together by forces between them rather like magnets), they find whatever pattern suits their shapes and their principal attracting points. They do this by random collisions; all sorts of arrangements are formed by chance, but most of them are dispersed again, and the one that persists and grows is the one having the lowest free energy, very often the one with the densest packing with least wasted space. The second method corresponds to the problem the crystallographer has when he tries to deduce the arrangement of the molecules by measuring the angles between the crystal faces and by other methods that will be described later on; he can deduce in a straightforward way the exact dimensions of the framework—the distances between similar points in the pattern, and the angles between the framework lines—and he then has to think how the molecules fit onto the framework.

The problems are simple enough when the motif of the crystal structure is a single spherical atom; as we have seen in an earlier chapter, the atoms of many metals fit in just as if they were billiard balls in contact, and build up to simple symmetrical structures. But when the molecule motifs are less simple in shape (as are some of those already illustrated), or when there are localized attracting points that favor particular positions or particular orientations of neighboring molecules, it is not so simple. What is the relation between the shape and symmetry of the motif and the geometry and symmetry of the repeating pattern that results from the ordered packing of the motifs? We have already seen that very often the symmetries of the molecules are not all utilized in the repeating pattern, and in fact some highly symmetrical molecules form crystals of low symmetry. The reason is that the dominating consideration is regularity, not symmetry. Molecules get together to form a repeating pattern having the lowest free energy, having regard to their shapes and their attracting points; it is regular because the mutual arrangement having the lowest free energy is the same everywhere, and it is based on a straight-line scheme because a repeating pattern *must* follow straight lines; but regularity and a straight-line framework need not imply symmetry. It is possible to have a repeating pattern which is perfectly regular but has no symmetry at all. Look at the flat pattern in Fig. 91 for instance; this has perfect regularity but no symmetry, and space patterns can be like this too. Nevertheless, the arrangements of molecules found in crystals do nearly always have

Fig. 91. A plane pattern which is perfectly regular but has no symmetry.

symmetries, sometimes quite complicated systems of symmetries, which are important because some of the symmetries of the internal pattern are displayed in the external shapes of the crystals and in other ways, and the investigator trying to discover the arrangement pounces on these clues. He then has to think how molecules of a particular type or shape (he often knows a good deal about the shape from chemical evidence) can pack together to form an arrangement having the symmetry which is his clue.

In any case, symmetry is fascinating for its own sake, and as a matter of fact, years before there was any possibility of discovering in detail the shapes of molecules, mathematicians (those who were interested in geometry) had thought out all the possible arrangements in space—the internal symmetries of all possible repeating patterns. Some people are like that; out of intellectual curiosity they set themselves problems like this, even when there is at the time no obvious use in the knowledge. They do these things partly because there is an intellectual exhilaration in solving problems (even pointless ones like crossword puzzles), but even more because they feel that there is something quite fundamental and eminently worthwhile in a problem of this sort, for it is concerned with the nature of things. Some mathematicians will maintain that their work is sufficient unto itself, quite apart from any possible use of the results for scientific or practical purposes; the underlying idea is that numbers, symmetries, and regularities are part of the nature of things and need no justification.

However, the problem of working out all the possible types of space patterns was not quite as abstract as all that. The three geometricians who quite independently thought them all out in the nineteenth century—the German Schönflies, the Englishman Barlow, and the Russian Fedorov—were all crystallographers, who must have realized the implications of their work even though, at the time, there was no possibility of utilizing the results. It was evident, from the external shapes of crystals, that there must be precise space patterns of particles inside. For chemically simple substances (like metals that grow cubic crystals) guesses about their structure could be made; for complicated substances there was little basis for even guessing, but all the same there must be a fascinating space pattern inside, and a thorough working out of all the possible space patterns must be relevant and might well be valuable some day. As it turned out, there were not very many years to wait before the results bore fruit, for the thinking out of the space patterns was done in the eighties and nineties of the last century, and the possibility of using the results became a real prospect with the discovery in 1912 that X-rays could reveal the internal structure of crystals. By the twenties of this century, the use of the results was well under way; we shall come to that later. Meanwhile, let us think of the subject simply from the point of view of pattern making.

To get a glimpse of the possibilities, think first about patterns on surfaces—the types of patterns that are familiar in wallpapers and curtain materials; and for a start, consider what can be done with a rectangular framework like that shown in Fig. 92 which has different dimensions in the vertical and horizontal directions. Use a motif that has no symmetry at all—for this is the pattern making game in its most general and most instructive form—and think of the ways of arranging motifs of this sort on the rectangular framework in appropriate groupings. The framework has two sets of planes of symmetry, one horizontal and one vertical (imagine them sticking out perpendicular to the page), and one obvious way of utilizing motifs that have no symmetry is to put four of them together so that the group has two planes of symmetry, and to place such a group at each station of the framework as in Fig. 92a. This arrangement seems appropriate because the symmetry of the group of motifs coincides with that of the framework. If the groups of motifs were tilted as in Fig. 92b, it would somehow not seem appropriate; the reason why it seems inappropriate is that the surroundings of motif 1 are now different from those of motif 2, and we feel that identical motifs ought to have identical surroundings. Our feeling of artistic appropriateness corresponds pretty well to the realities of interatomic forces in crystals, for identical molecules tend to arrange themselves so that their surroundings are identical; this is really the reason for the symmetries found in crystals; if molecules were tilted into "inappropriate" positions as in Fig. 92b, the forces between them would pull them into the "appropriate" positions of Fig. 92a.

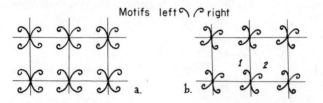

FIG. 92. (a) Groups of four asymmetric motifs arranged to form a pattern with a rectangular framework. (b) Tilted groups of motifs would not be appropriate for a rectangular framework.

It is not really essential to use four motifs in each group; consider the two-motif group in Fig. 93a. Although this has only one plane of symmetry, it does seem appropriate to the rectangular framework, because each motif again has the same surroundings as its neighbors; the one plane of symmetry in the group of motifs, coinciding with the plane of symmetry of the framework, justifies the rectangular character of the framework. If the framework were not rectangular, as in Fig. 93b, motif 1 would not have the same relation to its surroundings as motif 2. But one cannot go any further and use only one motif at each station of the framework as in Fig. 94a, because without

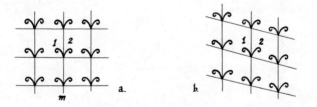

FIG. 93. (a) Reflection-related pairs of asymmetric motifs fit a rectangular framework. (b) A nonrectangular framework would not be appropriate for such pairs of motifs.

any symmetry there is no earthly reason why the framework should be rectangular. This is not playing the game, and if these motifs were molecules, they would pull the framework out of shape, spoiling the right angles (Fig. 94b). Nor can we use two motifs arranged as in Fig. 95a, because again there would be no

FIG. 94. (a) Single asymmetric motifs are not appropriate for a rectangular framework. (b) They are appropriate for a nonrectangular framework.

justification for the rectangular framework. This arrangement would be appropriate on a nonrectangular framework as in Fig. 95b.

So far, so good; but have we exhausted the possibilities of the rectangular framework? No, because if our criterion of appropriateness is that motifs shall all have identical surroundings, there are other things we can do. For instance, we can put groups of four motifs at the centers of the cells as well as the corners,

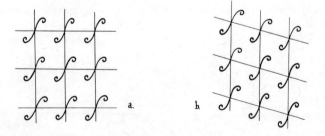

FIG. 95. A pair of motifs related by a center of symmetry is appropriate to the nonrectangular framework (b), not to the rectangular framework (a).

as in Fig. 96a; the rectangular framework is still justified. It is true that for this arrangement the real unit area of the pattern is the rhombus-shaped area *ABCD* which is nonrectangular; nevertheless it is symmetry that is all-important, and this "centered" pattern has the same symmetries as the simpler pattern of Fig. 92a, so it is justifiable to include it among the rectangular patterns. In a similar way the "centered" two-motif arrangement of Fig. 96b is on the same footing as the simple two-motif arrangement of Fig. 93a. These "centered" flat patterns correspond to the centered unit cells of crystals we have already met in Chapter 5.

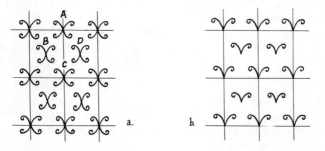

Fig. 96. Centered arrangements on a rectangular framework. (a) With both vertical and horizontal planes of symmetry. (b) With only vertical planes of symmetry.

There are still more possibilities that are appropriate to the rectangular framework. Instead of keeping pairs of motifs together as in Fig. 93a, we can separate them, moving one of them halfway along the cell edge as in Fig. 97a. This arrangement still obeys the rule that the surroundings of all motifs shall be the same (for the relation of motif 2 to motif 1 is exactly the same as that of 3 to 2), and so is still appropriate to the rectangular framework; if the motifs were molecules, the forces between them would not distort the framework. This sort of thing, which is much used in wallpaper patterns and the like, is something we have not met yet in this book; the relation between motifs 1 and 2 is no longer the plane of symmetry of the earlier arrangements, nor is it any of the types of symmetry we have discussed in earlier chapters; it is a new type of symmetry that can occur in repeating patterns but not in crystal shapes or isolated objects because it is a type of symmetry that involves *translation*. All the types of symmetry that have been mentioned earlier have been the symmetries possible in isolated, nonrepeating objects; their essential character is that if you go on repeating the symmetry operation you come back to the motif you first thought of: if you start with motif 1 in Fig. 93a and reflect it in the mirror plane *m*, you get to motif 2; reflect *this* in the mirror plane *m* and you find yourself back in motif 1. (And so it is with all the symmetry elements mentioned in Chapter 7; a fourfold rotation axis, for instance, would take you, after four repetitions, back to the object you started from.) But the new type of symmetry in Fig. 97a takes you, first from motif 1 to motif 2, then at the second repetition to motif 3; 3 is equivalent to 1 but is at the next station of the framework. By continuing the repetition, we should travel right through the pattern. This new type of symmetry is called the "glide plane"; imagine motif 1 first reflected by the plane *g* in Fig. 97b to position 1', then gliding halfway along the cell edge (exactly halfway) to become motif 2. Symmetry elements involving translation are of great importance in repeating patterns, whether in wallpapers or crystals. In wallpapers they "make the pattern flow" and avoid the stiffness that is a danger when only nontranslational elements are used, and in crystals we shall see that they occur more often than the nontranslational elements.

The glide planes could have been put along the short edges of the cell, giving the pattern in Fig. 97c; but this does not count as a different type of pattern—it is exactly equivalent to 97a in its symmetries.

Other ways of using glide planes to give different types of patterns are shown in Fig. 98, and with these we complete the list of flat patterns possible on a rectangular framework with unequal dimensions. There are seven; no more are possible. Notice that in Fig. 98a there are glide planes not only along the framework lines but also halfway between them; this often happens—if you specify symmetry elements in one set of positions, you find that inevitably there are others between them. Another point worth noticing is that in Fig. 98b the glide planes are not along the framework lines and halfway positions but at one-quarter and three-quarter positions; this again is something that often happens in patterns, whether on surfaces or in space— the symmetry elements do not have to coincide with the framework lines.

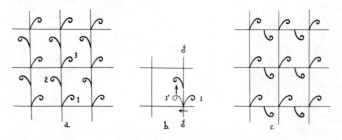

Fig. 97. Patterns with glide planes of symmetry. (a) This pattern has vertical glide planes of symmetry. (b) The operations necessary to convert motif 1 to motif 2. (c) This pattern has horizontal glide planes of symmetry.

The total number of types of symmetry in flat patterns is only seventeen. In addition to the seven rectangular ones and the two oblique ones in Figs. 94b and 95b, the only other ones have fourfold and sixfold axes of symmetry: there are three with fourfold axes and five with sixfold axes; we shall not go through them systematically, but one of the tetragonal patterns is shown in Fig. 99 for the sake of its decorative appeal. (Notice that the groups of motifs at the framework corners are right-handed, while those between them are left-handed; such an arrangement would not be called "centered" for this word is reserved for patterns in which all the groups are identical.) Other types of symmetry, such as fivefold or sevenfold axes, cannot exist in repeating patterns, as we have already seen in Chapter 7.

The plane patterns give a foretaste of what to expect in space patterns. The number of possibilities will of course be very much

greater, and if again we play the game in its most general form
by starting with motifs having no symmetry and using as many
as are required to make symmetrical groups, we can expect first
of all to find thirty-two arrangements corresponding to the
thirty-two crystal classes that were mentioned in Chapter 7.

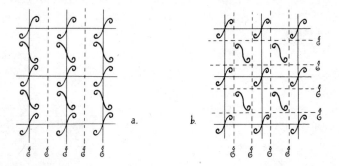

FIG. 98.   More patterns with glide planes. (a) With vertical glide
planes (g). (b) With both vertical and horizontal glide planes.

Arranging motifs or molecules to form isolated groups is formally
the same problem as arranging crystal faces to form a crystal
shape, and we can evidently make the first thirty-two space
patterns by forming groups of motifs or molecules having the
symmetries of the thirty-two types of crystal shape ("point-
groups," as they are called, because they are symmetry arrange-

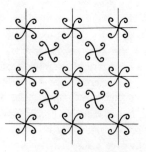

FIG. 99.   A pattern with tetragonal symmetry.

ments around isolated points), and placing them at the stations of the appropriate space framework or lattice. An arrangement of motifs or molecules having an axis of fourfold symmetry will appropriately go at the stations of a lattice (Fig. 100) having unit cells of tetragonal character, the three edges being all at

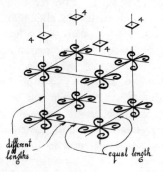

FIG. 100. A tetragonal space group. Two cell edges (the horizontal ones) equal, the third different.

right angles to each other, with two of them equal in length forming a square base and the third different. An arrangement having a twofold axis as its only element of symmetry can only go appropriately on a monoclinic lattice (Fig. 101); and so on.

But this is only a beginning; we are already prepared to find far more arrangements than this, for two reasons. In the first

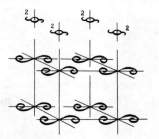

FIG. 101. A monoclinic space group. All cell edges unequal; one angle (the horizontal one) not a right angle.

place, we shall have to add the "centered" arrangements—those
with identical groups at the centers of the faces of the cell or at
the body center as well as at the corners. In the second place,
symmetry elements involving translation will very much increase
the numbers over and above the number of point groups, which
only involve nontranslational symmetry elements. One of the
translational symmetry elements, the glide plane, we have already
met in the flat patterns, but there are others which need the
three dimensions of space for their demonstration. These are
what are called screw axes of symmetry; in addition to the
ordinary rotation axes of symmetry like the threefold axis of the
Isle of Man symbol (Fig. 39), there can be in space patterns
threefold screw axes which, as the name implies, have a screw
or helical character. The three motifs, instead of being arranged
around the axis on the same level as in the ordinary rotation
axis, are placed at different levels around the screw axis (see
Fig. 102); to get from one to the next, you rotate one-third of

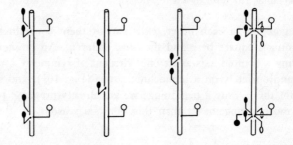

Fig. 102.   Threefold axes of symmetry. (The motifs are white on
one side and black on the other.)

a turn and move one-third of the way to the next station; the
three motifs, and their repetitions in the succeeding units, trace
out a screw or helix. (*Not* a "spiral," by the way—that would
be the wrong word; a spiral increases in diameter at each turn,
and can be flat like the hairspring of a watch, but a helix has a
constant diameter and is not flat. "Screw" is an appropriate
word provided that you think of a bolt having a constant diameter,

not a wood screw that tapers. The thing we call a spiral staircase ought to be called a helical staircase.)

There are, of course, two sorts of threefold screw axes, corresponding to left- and right-handed screws; both are shown in Fig. 102. They are equivalent but certainly not identical: a left-hand screw is left-handed whichever way you look at it. Just to complete the gallery of threefold symmetry axes that can occur in space patterns, a threefold alternating axis is also included in the figure; this sort of symmetry we have met before, in crystal shapes—see the picture of a calcite crystal in Fig. 48. The same symmetry can occur in arrangements of motifs or molecules in a space pattern.

Other screw axes that can occur in space patterns (and indeed have been found in many crystal structures) are twofold, fourfold, and sixfold. There are several types of fourfold and sixfold screw axis; we shall not consider all of them—they are mentioned to give some idea of the variety of symmetry possibilities there are in space patterns—but notice that the symmetry numbers involved are again restricted to 2, 3, 4, and 6, just as they are in ordinary rotation axes. Repeating patterns cannot have fivefold or more-than-sixfold screw axes, any more than they can have ordinary rotation axes with these symmetries. Isolated arrangements of motifs or molecules can have such symmetries—we can think of a screw arrangement of five flowers or a helical staircase with eleven steps to each turn—but such arrangements would not be appropriate in a repeating pattern, for the familiar reason that the surroundings could not possibly be the same for all the motifs. And once more, if the motifs were molecules, the differing forces between different pairs of motifs would tend to distort the pattern: an arrangement that started as a fivefold or elevenfold helix would tend to be pulled out of shape, probably to an asymmetric form, and even if its internal rigidity kept it pretty nearly to the original ideal fivefold or elevenfold helix, a space pattern composed of such helices could not have fivefold or elevenfold symmetry. In other words, the space pattern ignores symmetries that are incompatible with its own nature—it can do nothing else.

Finally there is the twofold screw axis. Notice that it is quite a different symmetry element from the glide plane. If we use motifs that are white on one side and black on the other to make them asymmetric, the screw axis gives us an arrangement which shows us (as in Fig. 103) the front of motif 1 and the back of motif 2, while the glide plane gives an arrangement which shows us the front of both motifs.

All these additional symmetry elements, together with the centered arrangements, make possible many more types of space patterns than the thirty-two point groups; but the number is still quite definite. The three crystallographers who systematically went through the possibilities at the end of the nine-

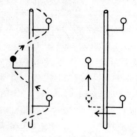

F𝐼G. 103. The twofold screw axis (*left*) is a different symmetry element from the glide plane (*right*).

teenth century used different procedures in their systems, but all came to the same answer: the number is two hundred and thirty. This number, it must be emphasized, is the number of *types* of space patterns—the number of space groups, as they are called. A space group is not a pattern, it is a group of symmetry elements which is the underlying basis for a pattern. The variety of actual patterns is of course infinite. The shapes and sizes of motifs even for any one space group are infinitely variable, and so are the relative dimensions and angles of the frameworks for the less symmetrical space groups; but the number of space groups is limited and quite definite.

Two examples of space groups are shown in Figs. 104 and 105. The first is orthorhombic (three unequal axes at right angles),

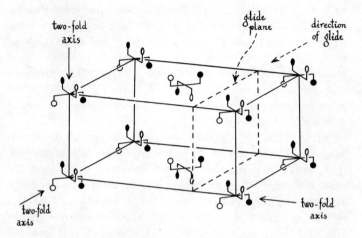

Fig. 104.   An orthorhombic space group with glide planes.

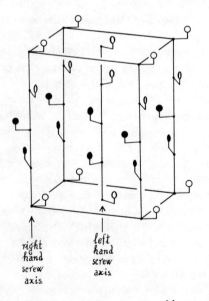

Fig. 105.   A tetragonal space group with screw axes.

and has glide planes and twofold axes, some of which are indicated. The second is tetragonal (all axes at right angles, two being equal in length and the third different), and has tetragonal screw axes. These are comparatively simple ones, each of them having eight asymmetric motifs in the unit cell. There are many that are much more complicated than this, especially in the more highly symmetrical systems. It takes a large number of asymmetric motifs to make up a space pattern with cubic symmetry—some of the cubic space groups take 96 or even as many as 192 to attain all the symmetry elements possible. But, quite apart from the difficulty of illustrating them on a flat surface, there is little point in exploring the ultimate possibilities. It is good to get a general idea of the principles and look at a few examples, but even professional scientists engaged in the subject do not usually go through the whole list; they look at a few examples, sufficient to convince themselves that they could grasp others if necessary, and leave it at that. The job has been done completely by others, and if one realizes the principles, one is in a position to utilize the results as occasion demands.

But enough of abstractions and symbolic motifs; let us get back to real molecules and see how far the arrangements in crystals correspond to the space groups that can in principle be designed. We now know the structure of many crystals, thanks to the use of X-rays in the way described in a later chapter; and the application of the systematic treatment of the space groups due to the earlier geometricians has been of the greatest value to the X-ray crystallographers in their attempts to solve the structural puzzles they have encountered; but you may well ask how many of the possible space groups have in fact been found. The answer is that examples of most of them are known, but that the more highly symmetrical space groups are not formed by molecules having no symmetry; it would take a lot of asymmetric molecules to build a cubic crystal, and in fact most of the completely asymmetric molecules build crystals of low symmetry—triclinic or monoclinic or orthorhombic— which need two or four or perhaps eight molecules to the unit cell.

Many examples of the highly symmetrical space groups are

known, but they are formed from molecules which are themselves highly symmetrical. Far fewer of such molecules are required to build a space group of high symmetry. An example is adamantane, which is a sort of cage of carbon atoms with hydrogen atoms attached on the outside; it is a molecule of tetrahedral symmetry which fits appropriately into a cubic structure of corresponding symmetry; matters are helped by its nearly spherical shape, leading to a face-centered cubic arrangement (Fig. 106). We could, if we liked, say that in such structures

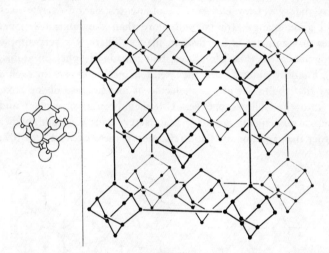

FIG. 106.   The structure of adamantane. (Hydrogen atoms are omitted.)

the asymmetric motif is a part of a molecule, perhaps quite a small part; formally this is perfectly correct, but it is simpler to say that fewer of such molecules are required to build a highly symmetrical space group. For some very simple substances which crystallize in highly symmetrical arrangements (like sodium chloride in Fig. 7, or some of the metals crystallizing as in Fig. 8), it could be said that the asymmetric motif is a small piece of an atom (sometimes, we should even have to say, it consists of small pieces of two or more different sorts of atoms!); but there is no point in doing so—this would be carrying formalism too far. In other words, there is no sense in playing the game of the symmetry elements in its most general form when the most general form is not necessary.

Although examples of many of the space groups are known, some of them are far more common than others. There are probably various reasons for this; the space groups that are found depend on the shapes and the attractive forces of the building units—atoms, molecules, and ions. One circumstance that seems to play an important part is suggested by the fact that the symmetry elements involving translation—screw axes and glide planes—are favored more than the nontranslational axes of symmetry and reflection planes. There is a very simple explanation for this. Molecules, being made of spherical atoms, are knobbly objects, and they tend to pack together in such a way that the knobs of one molecule fit into hollows of the next, or into the hollows between two neighboring molecules; and such arrangements usually mean screw axes or glide planes rather than rotation axes and reflection planes. Look at Fig. 107;

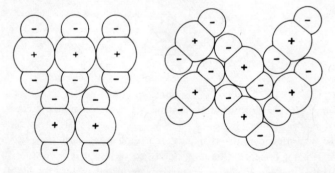

FIG. 107. *Left:* An arrangement that is unlikely, because it wastes space and violates electrostatic principles. *Right:* This one is better on both counts.

you would not expect the sort of packing on the left, where the knobs are opposite to each other, as they would be if the molecules were related by a rotation axis or reflection plane; this arrangement wastes space. The molecules can get closer if they pack as on the right. Furthermore, in molecules consisting of different atoms joined together, there are electrical polarities. Whenever two different atoms are joined, one is always electrically positive and the other negative. Suppose the big atoms are positive and the small ones negative; the arrangement on the left would put like atoms together, whereas the arrangement on the right allows the positive atoms of one molecule to come into contact with the negative atoms of the next (always the favored arrangement). This then is another circumstance which favors the sort of arrangement on the right in which the molecules are related by glide planes.

The sort of arrangement on the right-hand side of Fig. 107 is very common indeed. For very simple molecules like the two-atom ones of some of the elements, the arrangement is often fairly symmetrical; for chlorine and iodine it is orthorhombic—this has been illustrated in Fig. 21. For more complicated molecules the symmetry is more often monoclinic.

One thing that is very noticeable is that the symmetries of molecules are not all utilized in the arrangements in crystals. The naphthalene molecule, for instance (depicted earlier in Fig. 25), has three planes of symmetry, three twofold axes, and a center of symmetry—enough to qualify it for an orthorhombic arrangement if these symmetries were utilized; but nearly all of them are ignored—the only one used in the monoclinic arrangement is the center of symmetry. The reason is presumably that the monoclinic arrangement fulfills the requirements of the satisfaction of local points of attraction and of good packing better than some other arrangements that could utilize more of the natural symmetries of the molecules. In principle, one could expect that in an arrangement like this the molecule might be distorted by the forces around it, but this molecule happens to be a very rigid one and is not appreciably distorted. Planes of symmetry and axes of symmetry in molecules are very often ignored in the formation of crystal space patterns, but centers of symmetry are utilized, more often than not.

Molecules with no symmetry at all tend to form crystals of low symmetry, as I have already said. A good example is penicillin, the familiar drug with powerful bactericidal effects. It is the sodium salt of a complicated acid, the molecules of which have no symmetry at all but are roughly U-shaped (Figs. 108 and 119). The acid group and some other oxygen atoms lie around the bend of the U, while the ends of the U are hydrocarbon in character (like gasoline or benzene). These molecules pack together in a monoclinic arrangement which illustrates some of the principles of packing. The acid parts of the molecules, which have negative electric charges, are grouped with the positively charged sodium ions around twofold screw axes (Fig. 108A), while the uncharged hydrocarbon parts of the molecules are directed away from the acid parts and also group themselves around twofold screw axes (Fig. 108B).

Small molecules like those considered so far cannot have screw axes or glide planes of symmetry; but the molecules in plastics and fibers, which are very long chains in which a particular group of atoms is repeated many times along the chain, can possess these types of symmetry, and when the chain molecules arrange themselves in regular crystalline fashion, these translational types of symmetry are sometimes utilized. In a sense the crystal is already in existence in one direction, and since the translational types of symmetry are favored in crystal structures, it is not surprising that they are utilized. Two examples of these chain molecules are shown in Fig. 109; the polystyrene molecule has a helical form displaying a threefold screw axis, and this is utilized in a crystal structure of trigonal symmetry; the molecule of polyvinyl chloride has a glide plane, which is utilized in an orthorhombic structure.

The preference for screw axes and glide planes in crystals composed of molecules (as opposed to those composed of ions) is very marked indeed, and of the hundreds of crystals whose structures are now known, most of them crystallize in patterns having the space groups containing only these translational elements of symmetry, or else combinations of the translational elements with centers of symmetry (for the center of symmetry is another type of symmetry element that allows good packing with the knobs of one molecule fitting into hollows of another).

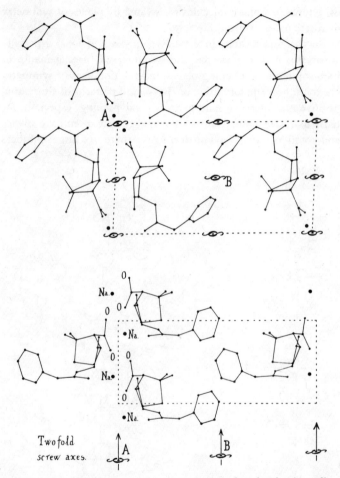

FIG. 108. Two views of the arrangement of molecules in sodium penicillin. The crystals are monoclinic, and the only symmetry in the arrangement is a set of twofold screw axes. *Upper:* the arrangement as seen along the screw axes; *lower:* a side view. Negatively charged oxygen atoms and positively charged sodium atoms are grouped around the screw axes marked A, while the hydrocarbon parts of the molecules are grouped around the screw axes marked B. (More "solid-looking" pictures of an individual penicillin molecule, from two different view points, are shown in Fig. 119).

Structures in which molecules are related by planes of symmetry or rotational axes are quite rare.

On the other hand, in crystals composed of ions, especially when the ions are simple and symmetrical, arrangements of high symmetry containing planes and rotation axes of symmetry are common. The formation of chessboard patterns of alternating positive and negative ions permits good packing, especially for particular size ratios; and such arrangements often have planes and rotation axes of symmetry. Since there are large numbers

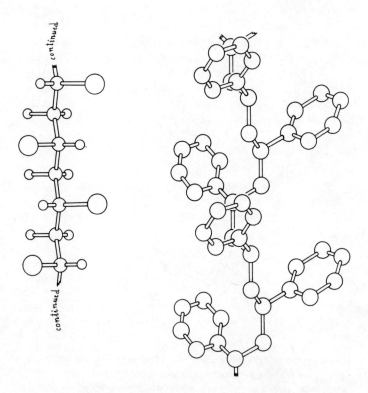

FIG. 109. *Left:* Part of a molecule of polyvinyl chloride, a chain molecule thousands of atoms long. It has a glide plane of symmetry. *Right:* Polystyrene. This molecule has a threefold screw axis of symmetry.

of simple salts of this type, they swell the ranks of the highly symmetrical cubic and hexagonal space groups.

The great value of the systematic and complete catalogue of all space groups, with their symmetries and the relative positions and orientations of the motifs, is twofold. In the first place, those who investigate the structures of crystals have all the possibilities in front of them; there is always the danger, in an *ad hoc* investigation, that a particular solution of the structural puzzle that occurs to the investigator and which satisfies some of the evidence will be pursued exclusively, and if it turns out eventually to be wrong and he has to start again, a great deal of time may have been wasted. When a complete catalogue is available, there is no excuse for missing other possible solutions; they can be considered from the start, and probably a better choice can be made of the best one to investigate first. Secondly, there are systematic and straightforward ways of detecting symmetry elements by X-rays, and when this kind of evidence has revealed a particular combination of symmetry elements, the catalogue of space groups shows just what sort of a pattern it is that has this combination of symmetry elements. This is an immense help, and the investigator then has a firm basis on which to consider how the molecules he knows to be there can fit in. This subject is taken up in the next chapter.

CHAPTER 13

X-Ray Revelation:
How Atomic Space-Patterns
Are Discovered

The arrangements of the atoms and molecules in many different kinds of crystals have been illustrated and discussed in the preceding pages. We have accepted the results of a great deal of work without inquiring how the knowledge was obtained, except for the bare statement that it was obtained by using X-rays. There were good reasons for postponing an account of this very important part of the subject of crystallography to this point in the story; many of the interesting features of crystals —their shapes, their manner of growth, and the effects of light— can be described, and understood up to a point, without inquiring into the precise details of the atomic space patterns or the methods used in unraveling these details, though I have not hesitated to use the available knowledge where it helped in the exposition. Indeed, much of the existing knowledge about crystals was gained long before it was possible to find out anything about the atomic patterns in detail.

Some sort of space pattern there obviously was: the polyhedral shapes of crystals hinted at it, and the fact that the only shape symmetries found in crystals are those based on internal repeating patterns left no reasonable doubt. Moreover, measurement of the angles between the faces of a crystal led to a knowledge of the shape of the unit cell, or at any rate a possible unit cell. But until the discovery of X-rays and their effects on crystals, it was not possible to know the *size* of the unit cell or anything about the motifs composing the unit of pattern. It was known, for instance, that in the ammonium sulfate crystal the unit cell is a rectangular box with its three different edge lengths in the ratios 0.5635 : 1 : 0.7319, but the size of the box was unknown; it might be a small one containing one molecule of high symmetry, or a larger one with many molecules (perhaps of lower symmetry) in an intricate arrangement.

The discovery that X-rays, on passing through a crystal, are diverted from their original direction into other directions making a pattern of "diffracted" rays that could be used for finding out the details of the internal atomic pattern was a dramatic one, made in 1912 by Max von Laue in Munich; the story of the events that led up to it and of the developments that followed it is one of the sagas of our time. X-Rays had been discovered 17 years earlier by Röntgen, and their power of penetrating through substances that are opaque to light was soon utilized, especially in medicine for revealing details inside living creatures; but the nature of X-rays was, in the early years of this century, a great puzzle. The discovery of X-rays was one of the many results of experiments on sending electric currents through moderately evacuated tubes by applying a high voltage between metal electrodes. The remaining air is split up into the little negatively charged particles called electrons and positively charged remnants, and the passing of the current is due to the movement of the electrons from the negative metal electrode to the positive one and the opposite movement of the positively charged remnants; when the electrons strike the positive electrode (the "target")—which they do at high speed owing to the high voltage used to accelerate them—the X-rays are given off from the target in all directions. To find out the nature of these new rays, many experiments were carried out to measure the properties, in the hope of finding clues to settle the question of whether the rays are waves like light or particles like electrons; but up to 1912 conclusive evidence had not been found. Their path was apparently not refracted (bent) on passing from one substance to another, and therefore if they were waves they must either be extremely different in length from light waves or else be of a different nature. Neither were they diverted from their path by electrical or magnetic fields as electrons were, so they were not electrically charged particles. The principal knowledge that had been gained by physicists was of their penetrating power in all sorts of materials; quite a lot was known about this, but it did not settle the question of whether they were particles or waves.

The situation was somewhat similar to that which existed a century earlier in relation to light. The experiments which demonstrated the wave nature of light were experiments in which the interference of waves (cancellation in some directions and reinforcement in others) was recognized. The physicists of the early years of this century were of course well aware of this, but what could they use to produce interference effects with X-rays? Waves only give interference effects if they are scattered by objects about the same distance apart as the length of the waves. Attempts to produce interference effects by passing X-rays through extremely narrow slits were unsuccessful, and from this failure it could only be concluded that if X-rays were waves like light, their wavelength must be extremely short, at most one-thousandth that of light, or the one hundred millionth part of a centimeter in length. On the other hand, it was known that X-rays ionize air strongly—that is, they split molecules of air and other gases into electrically negative electrons and electrically positive remnants, enabling the gases to conduct electricity; this behavior suggested that X-rays might be particles which break up gas molecules by colliding with them, and many physicists inclined to this view.

Laue, a young lecturer in physics at the time, was consulted by one of his students (Paul Ewald) about a problem in crystal optics, and this discussion directed Laue's attention to the internal structure of crystals which until this time he had hardly thought about. The puzzle of the nature of X-rays was very much "in the air" at Munich, for their discoverer Röntgen was a professor there; and Laue, becoming conscious for the first time that crystals were supposed to be repeating patterns of atoms, knew also that the distance between atoms was something like the one hundred millionth part of a centimeter—much the same magnitude as the upper limit for the wavelength of X-rays, if they *were* waves. The X-rays might, for all he knew, be much shorter than this, but at any rate it seemed worthwhile to send a narrow beam of X-rays through a crystal to see whether interference effects would be produced.

He did not know quite what sort of effects to expect, for scattering by a three-dimensional pattern is a very different matter from scattering by passing through a simple slit or hole; moreover, it was known from absorption experiments that the X-rays were mixed, containing components of different penetrating power (different wavelengths?), and also that when X-rays pass through substances containing certain atoms, they are partly converted into different X-rays of different penetrating power (different wavelengths?). Both these circumstances might confuse or totally obscure any interference effects. Never mind; try it and see what happens!

The crystal chosen for the first experiment was hydrated copper sulfate, the familiar blue substance; and Laue's students Friedrich and Knipping arranged to send a narrow X-ray beam through this crystal (using small holes in lead screens to cut the X-ray beam down to a narrow pencil of rays) and to detect any scattered rays by photographic plates placed in likely positions. Plates in most positions showed nothing, but a plate placed so that it caught the direct beam which came through the crystal (see Fig. 110) showed, in addition to the very black central spot due to the direct beam, some extra spots much weaker than the central one. They certainly looked like interference effects, for

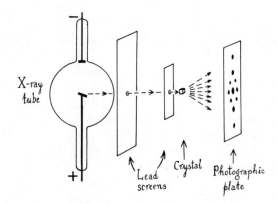

FIG. 110.   Laue's experiment.

they were of various intensities, and when it was found that a
tilt of the crystal caused the spots to move, it was evident that
these spots had something to do with the patterned structure
of the crystal.

Further progress was not easy, for as a matter of fact they
could hardly have made a worse choice than hydrated copper
sulfate for the first experiment, as it is a crystal of very low
symmetry (triclinic) and is chemically rather complex. It was
soon evident that, to have a reasonable chance of detailed understanding of what was happening, they must use more symmetrical
crystals of simpler composition; so they tried several cubic
crystals, and sure enough, obtained patterns of spots with fourfold symmetry when they sent the X-ray beam along cube axes,
and patterns of threefold symmetry when the beam was sent
along a cube diagonal (which is an axis of threefold symmetry).
Examples of Laue patterns are shown in Plate 9; the symmetry
of the diffraction pattern reveals very clearly the symmetry of
the crystal for the direction chosen. There was now little doubt
that they were getting interference effects, and their results
opened the way in a dramatic manner to the exploration of two
great subjects—the nature of X-rays, which were evidently very
short waves, and the internal structure of crystals. The story
is an example of a situation that is not uncommon: it is often
necessary to solve two big problems at the same time, for the
vital evidence for each depends on the other. A century earlier,
the strange effects of crystals on light played an equally vital
role in revealing the nature of light waves and their polarization.

The effect of a regular pattern on waves of any sort is not a
familiar phenomenon in everyday life, but it can be observed
quite easily by simply looking at a distant point of light through
a handkerchief or any fine-meshed material held close to your
eye; you can see not one point of light but many, arranged in
a square formation. It is not the mesh of the material you can
see, for (quite apart from the fact that the material is too close
for you to focus on it) the size of the array of light spots remains
unchanged if you move the handkerchief further from your eye;
moreover, if you try again with a finer meshed material, the

light spots are farther away from each other, not nearer. Nevertheless, the square arrangement of light spots is *due to* the square mesh of the material; the many images of the light mean that the light waves are diverted from their original direction into a number of other directions which are arranged in a square formation just because the mesh of the handkerchief is a square one. The diversion into a number of separate directions means that the light waves act together in these directions but cancel each other in intermediate directions; the whole process is called "diffraction," and this is the word we shall use. The light spots are very close together; this is because the mesh of the handkerchief is a good deal larger than the wavelength of light; if a finer meshed fabric is used, the spots are further apart—the "diffraction pattern" is larger; there is always this inverse relation between the scale of the pattern in the material and the spread of the diffraction pattern.

Another thing to notice, when you look at a distant point of light through a handkerchief, is that if the light you are looking at is a white one, the diffraction pattern is somewhat confused by color effects; this is because the longer-wave light near the red end of the spectrum is diverted more than the shorter-wave light near the violet end; if you look at a distant sodium light, which gives orange waves of one wavelength only, the diffraction pattern is quite sharp. The spot patterns that Laue obtained when he sent X-rays through cubic crystals were of this nature, but they were more spread out because the wavelength of X-rays matched the "mesh" of the crystal structures more closely than in the handkerchief experiment with light. Another point of similarity is that Laue's X-rays were of mixed wavelengths, just as white light contains mixed wavelengths, and in the Laue X-ray diffraction patterns shown in Plate 9, each spot is due to a different wavelength; just as in the handkerchief experiment with light, each color is diverted to a different extent.

Laue worked out in principle the mathematics of the interference of waves scattered by a simple three-dimensional array of scattering centers, but before crystal structures could be deduced, some complexities had to be sorted out: a practical way of handling the mathematics had to be devised, the composition of the X-ray beam (the mixture of wavelengths in it) had to be found, and some information about the relative scattering efficiencies of different atoms was required. These vital contributions were made by W. H. Bragg (afterward Sir William) in Leeds and his son W. L. Bragg (afterward Sir Lawrence) in Cambridge, who took up the subject as soon as Laue's discovery was announced. W. L. Bragg suggested that the diffracted X-ray beams could be regarded as reflections by sheets of atoms in the crystal, and that from this point of view the mathematics of diffraction became extremely simple; the Bragg equation connecting the angle of diffraction (θ) with the X-ray wavelength (λ) and the spacing of the successive sheets of atoms (d) has been used ever since then, as the simplest way of handling the problems. It is an equation as simple as anyone could wish:

$$\sin \theta = \frac{n\lambda}{2d}$$

where n can be 1, 2, 3, or any other whole number.

The sheets of atoms in a crystal act as "X-ray mirrors," but there is an important point of difference between this sort of reflection and the more familiar reflection of light by a glass mirror. Ordinary light of any wavelength is reflected by a glass mirror at *any* angle of incidence, and if the mirror is tilted, the reflected ray is still there, though it comes off at a different angle. When X-rays encounter sheets of atoms in a crystal, the situation is different: reflection occurs only at special angles. There are many "X-ray mirrors," one behind the other at a definite spacing, and unless the angle of the beam and the wavelength are just right to suit the spacing, waves reflected by one mirror are not in step with those from the next, and the net result of many reflections progressively more and more out of step is complete cancellation; only when the angle and the wavelength are just right to suit the spacing is there cooperation of the waves reflected by the many successive sheets. This is the situation of which the Bragg equation is the quantitative expression.

With these ideas, W. L. Bragg turned to the problems of the crystal structures, and found that he could explain the Laue diffraction pattern of rocksalt (sodium chloride) if the X-ray beam contained a continuous range of wavelengths (like white light). What happens when a "white" X-ray beam goes through a crystal is that most of the wavelengths are, so to speak, wasted and pass straight on, but certain wavelengths are reflected— those that happen to suit the spacings of the sheets of atoms and the angle between the beam and sheets (Fig. 111). The

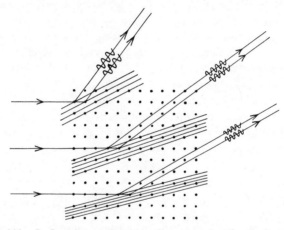

FIG. 111. In Laue's experiment, each spot on the plate is due to the reflection of X-rays by a different set of atomic planes acting as X-ray mirrors. The more widely spaced planes reflect the longer waves in the beam, while the more closely spaced planes reflect the shorter waves, at smaller angles.

crystal, so to speak, picks out the wavelengths it can reflect and ignores the rest. But what spacings were there in rocksalt? It was natural to try out the simple "chessboard" structure which had been suggested (as a speculation) years before by the English crystallographers Pope and Barlow (it has been illustrated earlier in this book, in Fig. 7), and it was found that this did account not only for the positions of the diffraction spots but also for their relative intensities if it was assumed that the diffracting powers of sodium and chlorine atoms are in the ratio of their atomic weights; the intensity of each spot depends on the positions of the two sorts of atoms in the structure and on their diffracting powers.

The assumption that the X-ray beam contained a continuous range of wavelengths was shown to be correct by W. H. Bragg in a different type of experiment; he constructed an X-ray spectrometer with a large rocksalt crystal to reflect the X-rays and an ionization chamber containing a suitable gas to measure the reflected rays (Fig. 112). By rotating the crystal he was able to reflect the different wavelengths in turn, and by rotating the ionization chamber at twice the speed to catch the reflected rays he could measure the intensity of each wavelength; in this way he showed that the beam did indeed contain a continuous range of wavelengths. But he found also something else of great importance: superimposed on the continuous range of wavelengths are a few very intense components of very sharply defined wavelengths. The actual wavelengths of these sharp components

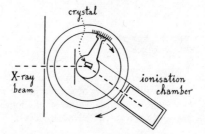

FIG. 112.   The Bragg X-ray spectrometer.

depend on the material of the target of the X-ray tube, and some metals, if the voltage across the tube is above a certain critical limit, give one outstandingly strong component (actually a very close doublet, but so close as to be regarded as monochromatic for most purposes). The importance of this was that it led to the possibility of using for many experiments an effectively monochromatic beam, thus simplifying the problems considerably.

(It also led to other great discoveries, for the study of the wavelengths of the sharp components given by different target metals opened a new chapter of our knowledge of the internal electronic structure of atoms; but that is another story.)

All these experiments left no doubt of the wave nature of X-rays; but, just as for visible light, some of the properties of X-rays indicated a particle nature as well. In fact, X-rays and visible light are both electromagnetic waves of exactly the same nature, differing only in wavelength, the X-rays being about one-thousandth of the length of visible light waves; both exist only in definite small amounts called quanta or photons, which behave as particles in some circumstances but waves in others. Nowadays the particle aspect of X-rays is very evident, for we often measure the intensity of an X-ray beam by actually counting the quanta by a Geiger counter.

Although the structures of several simple crystals were deduced successfully by W. L. Bragg from the Laue diffraction patterns of stationary crystals, it was soon realized that if only one wavelength were used the problems would be simplified; but with a single wavelength, reflections would only be obtained if the crystal were rotated to give each crystal plane a chance of being for a short time at the appropriate angle to reflect the one wavelength. When a crystal rotates in a monochromatic beam, in most positions nothing happens, but every now and then, when the angle suits the wavelength and the spacing of a particular set of "X-ray mirrors," a reflection flashes out. This has become the standard way of investigating crystal structures. A crystal is set up on a goniometer and adjusted so that one of its unit cell edges is parallel to the axis of rotation; this is most often done by using the reflections of light from its faces, as in the measurement of crystal angles illustrated earlier in Fig. 36. The X-ray beam is then turned on, and the crystal rotated slowly in it; as it turns, first one set of planes comes into a reflecting position and then others, (see Fig. 113) and the intensities of the reflections are measured. From the angles of reflection, the spacings of the various sets of planes can be calculated, and this leads fairly straightforwardly to an accurate knowledge of the dimensions

of the unit cell. To find the positions of the atoms with respect
to each other, it is necessary to consider the intensities of the
various reflections; some planes give strong reflections and others
weak ones, and this information constitutes a set of clues for
the solution of the puzzle of the crystal structure. To get enough
clues, it is usually necessary to do more than one rotation experiment; the crystal is rotated about two or more different axes
in turn, to get information from many different types of crystal
planes, oriented in all possible directions.

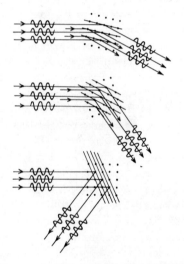

Fig. 113. When a crystal is rotated in a monochromatic X-ray
beam, the various planes of atoms are able to reflect only at particular
angles; the angle at which reflection takes place depends on the spacing
of the planes. The more widely spaced planes give reflections near the
primary beam; the more closely spaced planes reflect at the larger angles.

To see how the intensities of the different reflections depend
on the positions of the atoms, let us consider a very simple structure, that of ammonium chloride. This substance, the principal
constituent of the paste of "dry" batteries, usually crystallizes
in the fernlike branching growths shown in Plate 8, but when
there is urea in the solution it comes out as perfect cubes. Its

structure was not one of the first to be solved, but it is a particularly simple one, simpler in some ways than those that *were* solved first. It consists of chlorine ions and ammonium ions in equal numbers; an ammonium ion consists of a nitrogen atom with four hydrogen atoms attached to it, but we shall ignore the hydrogen atoms because they scatter X-rays so feebly that they make little difference; our concern is with the nitrogens and chlorines, their positions and their scattering powers.

The unit cell is a small cube containing only one chlorine and one nitrogen; if we choose the chlorine as the corner of the unit cell, the nitrogen is right at the center, as in Fig. 114a.

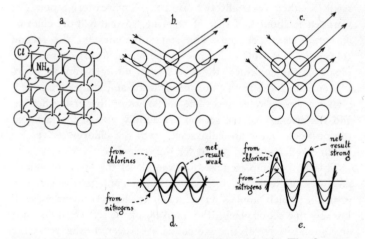

FIG. 114. (a) The structure of ammonium chloride. The first two X-ray reflections are from the atomic planes shown in (b) and (c); and the reason why the first is weak and the second strong is shown in (d) and (e).

The first X-ray reflection, the one at the smallest angle to the primary beam, comes from the set of planes shown in Fig. 114b and is not a very strong one. The next reflection comes from the set of planes in Fig. 114c and is very much stronger. The reason for the difference of intensity is shown in Figs. 114d and 114e. The first reflection flashes out when the waves reflected by the chlorines are all in step with each other; but when this happens, the nitrogens, which are in planes halfway between the chlorine planes, reflect waves which are half a wavelength behind those from the chlorines and are therefore completely out of step. If we represent the waves as in (d) and (e), the result of the combination of nitrogen and chlorine reflections is obtained by adding or subtracting the heights of the waves depending on whether there are crests or troughs at any particular point; and since for the first reflection, the nitrogen waves are completely out of step (or, as we say, exactly opposite in phase), they are subtracted from the chlorine waves, giving as a net result a rather weak reflection as in (d). The scattering power of nitrogen is about half that of chlorine, so that half the chlorine amplitude is wiped out. The state of affairs for the second reflection (e) is quite different, for the nitrogens are on the same planes as the chlorines; the waves from nitrogens are therefore in step with those from chlorines, and the amplitudes are added, giving a strong reflection. The weakness of the first reflection and the strength of the second are simply due to the fact that the nitrogen waves are subtracted from the chlorine waves for the first reflection and added for the second.

This is the simplest possible example of the effect of atomic positions on reflection intensities, but it contains the essential principle which applies to all crystals, however complicated. For any one set of planes, the intensity of the reflection depends on the positions of the atoms with respect to the reflecting planes, and of course on the scattering powers of the atoms. If, in the ammonium chloride type of structure, the atoms in the center of the unit cell scatter X-rays very much more feebly than those at the corners, the first reflection will be stronger and the second not quite so strong as in the ammonium chloride crystal; but if the center atoms scatter nearly as strongly as the corner atoms, the first reflection will be very weak and the second very strong. In the crystals of certain metals, of which iron is one, the arrangement is of this type and the center atoms are exactly the same as the corner atoms; the waves scattered by the center atoms are just as strong as those from the corner atoms and, being exactly out of step (or, as we say, exactly opposite in phase), completely wipe out the waves from the corner atoms, so that the first reflection is absent altogether. In more complicated crystals, there are various atoms distributed between the reflecting planes at fractional intervals, and the net amplitude of a reflection is the result of the addition of a number of waves out of step by different amounts, as in Fig. 115.

The structures of many simple crystals were worked out by thinking about the intensities of a few reflections in this way. The investigators had to think backward, of course; from the measured intensities they had to think what arrangement of atoms could give intensities of the right magnitudes, but for

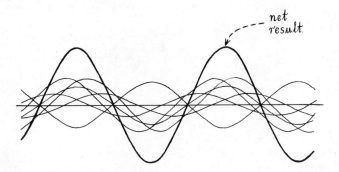

FIG. 115. For complex crystals, the net wave for any particular reflection is the result of a combination of a number of waves out of step by different amounts.

simple structures this was not too difficult once the way had been shown by W. L. Bragg. As time went on and crystallographers tackled more and more complex structures, it was necessary to measure many more reflections and to devise methods for thinking their way through a rather unwieldy mass of evidence.

The problem of collecting the evidence and making sure which type of crystal plane each X-ray reflection comes from (and remember that for a really complex crystal the number of

reflections may run into hundreds or even thousands) was solved
experimentally by the construction of ingenious X-ray gonio-
meters. An early arrangement (which is still used for some
purposes) is shown in Fig. 116; the X-ray beam is sent through
the crystal at right angles to its axis of rotation and the reflections
are recorded on a cylindrical photographic film surrounding the
crystal. The reflections on the straightened-out film are arranged
in straight lines parallel to the equator (see Plate 10); those *on*
the equator come from vertical crystal planes—those parallel to
the crystal's axis of rotation—while those above and below the
equator come from sloping planes. Thus the position of a reflection on the film shows, up to a point, what sort of crystal plane
it comes from. However, this does not pin it down completely;

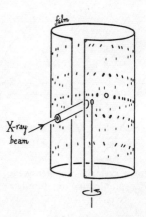

Fig. 116.   Arrangement for recording diffraction pattern given by
a crystal rotating in a monochromatic X-ray beam.

to do this it is necessary to have a more elaborate apparatus,
and several types have been devised in which one set of reflections
at a time is isolated by a screen with a slot in it, and the film
is moved in step with the rotation of the crystal. When the film
is developed, the reflection spots appear on it in a definite
arrangement, and the position of each reflection tells the crystallographer precisely which crystal plane it comes from, so that he

can collect all the information he needs in a straightforward, almost automatic way. What he needs to deduce the arrangement of atoms in a crystal is a complete set of reflections; the intensities of the reflections constitute the raw material needed to solve the puzzle of the crystal structure.

A photograph obtained in one of the most ingenious goniometer cameras of this type is shown in Plate 11; the spots are arranged in a straight-line pattern reminding one of the lattice structure of the crystal; it is *not* a picture of the crystal structure, but the lattice arrangement is related to the crystal structure in the same sort of way as the diffraction pattern seen by looking at a point of light through a handkerchief is related to the mesh structure of the handkerchief fabric. The closer the spots in the diffraction pattern the larger the mesh of the handkerchief or the unit cell of the crystal. The crystallographer's job is, so to speak, to turn the diffraction pattern inside out, to deduce the structure of the crystal it came from.

This process of turning a diffraction pattern inside out to get at the structure of the crystal it came from is straightforward enough as far as the shape and size of the unit cell are concerned; it entails only elementary calculations, and there are no uncertainties. But this is only the beginning, and the rest of the problem—the task of deducing the positions of all the atoms in the unit cell from the intensities of the diffraction spots—is usually far from straightforward, and may be a matter of great difficulty. The difficulty is not that the calculations are complex and laborious; they *are* complex and laborious, but that is no barrier; it used to mean a lot of work for someone, but nowadays it only means another job for an electronic computer, which makes light of such work. No, the trouble is that usually we do not have all the evidence necessary for a *direct* solution, and the problem has to be solved indirectly by fitting clues together. The clues are the intensities of all the many diffraction spots, and to deduce the positions of the atoms from them is rather like trying to solve a three-dimensional crossword puzzle (if you can imagine such a thing) in which each clue comes, not from one region of the crossword, but from the entire array of letters.

Each clue in the diffraction pattern—the intensity of each diffraction spot—is settled not by any one atom or even a local group of atoms but by the entire array in the unit cell. When there are many atoms in the unit cell, as there are in crystals of sugars and vitamins and proteins, the problems involved may seem to be of bewildering complexity.

The nature of the missing evidence may be appreciated by remembering that each diffraction spot represents a train of waves reflected by a particular set of crystal planes; and a train of waves has two characteristics: its amplitude (the intensity is proportional to the square of the amplitude—double the amplitude means four times the intensity), and its phase with respect to the crystal plane it comes from. The word phase expresses which part of the wave is *at* the plane in question, whether it is a crest or a trough or some intermediate point of the wave. The intensity of each diffraction spot is easily measured—it is proportional to the degree of blackness on a photographic film or the reading on a Geiger counter; but it is not possible to measure the phase. If we knew the amplitude and phase of all the diffracted waves from all the different crystal planes, we could calculate a picture of the crystal structure (showing the positions of all the atoms) in a direct manner; there is a straightforward mathematical way (called Fourier inversion) of turning a diffraction pattern inside out to give a picture of the structure, when both amplitude and phase are known for every diffracted wave. But unless the phase is known as well as the amplitude, this cannot be done; if the wrong phases were used, the wrong picture would be obtained; for every different combination of phases (crests for some crystal planes, troughs for others—and there are many possible combinations when there are many different planes) there is a different picture, and only one of them is correct.

We cannot measure phases experimentally; but for some types of crystal structure we can know them without measuring them. The simplest example is again the ammonium chloride crystal, which we have already used as a "guinea pig" crystal. Suppose now that we do not know the structure and want to deduce it.

When the size of the cubic unit cell is calculated from the positions of the diffraction spots, it is found that its size and weight are such that it contains only one chlorine and one nitrogen atom. If the corner of the unit cell is chosen to be the center of the chlorine atom, the problem is to find the nitrogen. Knowing that the diffracting power of nitrogen is much less than that of chlorine, we can be sure that, wherever it is in the cell, it can only wipe out something like half the amplitude of the chlorine wave, even at the worst when the nitrogen wave is exactly opposite in phase, as in Fig. 114d; the chlorine wave is reduced to half the amplitude without a change of phase; the nitrogen wave can never reverse the phase because it is not strong enough. We can say therefore that for every diffracted wave from every crystal plane, the phase is the same—there is a crest at the corner of the unit cell where the chlorine is. If all the diffracted waves are put together in the Fourier inversion equation, each with its own amplitude (obtained from the intensity) and all with the same phase, the result is a picture of the structure showing the nitrogen at the expected place at the centre of the cell. Actually this structure is so simple that there is no need to use this sledge-hammer method to crack such a small nut; but the example does show the essential principle, which applies equally well to complicated crystals. The picture obtained shows the electron densities throughout the unit cell, because it is the electrons in the atoms that scatter the X-rays; at the center of the cell where the nitrogen is, it shows an electron density peak about half the density of the one at the corner where the chlorine is.

The principle can be applied to quite complicated crystal structures with large numbers of atoms in the unit cell; if there is one atom that scatters X-rays very much more strongly than any of the others, this atom will dominate the situation as far as the phases of the waves are concerned; the wave from the strongly scattering atom (a heavy atom containing many electrons, like lead or mercury or bromine or iodine) will be so strong that the waves from all the other atoms, even if they reduce its intensity, cannot reverse its phase; it can be assumed that all the diffracted waves have the phase given by the heavy

atom, and on this basis a picture of the structure can be calculated
in a straightforward way by Fourier inversion. Many complex
structures have been solved in this way; the prospects of being
able to solve a really complex structure are immensely greater
when a heavy atom is present than when all the atoms are of
much the same weight. An early example of a structure solved
in this way is shown in Fig. 117; the complicated molecule is
known as phthalocyanine, which is the basis of some very good
pigments, especially a blue one (much used in paints) which is
a combination of this molecule with copper. A copper atom is

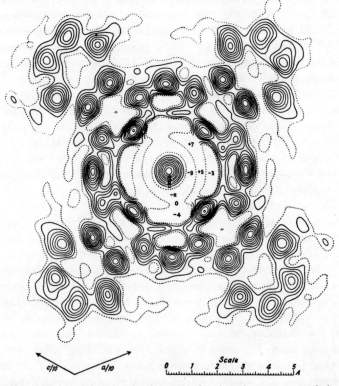

FIG. 117. An electron density map showing the structure of the
molecule of platinum phthalocyanine. The peak at the center (the platinum atom) is really very much higher than any of the others.

not heavy enough to dominate the phases, so a platinum atom was substituted in place of the copper in the center of the molecule. The result (obtained by J. M. Robertson in 1935) is shown as a contour map of electron densities; the atoms show up like mountain peaks on a geographical map, and the regular structure of the molecule with its interlinked rings of atoms is beautifully displayed.

The number of crystals having just one heavy atom among a number of lighter atoms in the unit cell is limited; more often, the unit cell contains several molecules, and if each of them contains one heavy atom, the problem is first of all to find the positions of the heavy atoms; if this can be done, it can then be assumed that the wave from the combined heavy atoms dominates the phases of all the reflections, and from this point the calculation of the rest of the structure proceeds in the straightforward way described in the preceding paragraphs. But the arrangement and the exact positions of the heavy atoms have to be found first; moreover, in the many crystals consisting entirely of atoms with not very dissimilar scattering powers, the whole process of finding the structure has to be accomplished without the aid of phase-dominating atoms. It is an indirect process that has to be approached in a puzzle-solving manner by looking for clues, proposing provisional assumptions, thinking out the consequences of them, and comparing the consequences with the evidence.

Many of the simpler crystal structures have been solved in this way, by "trial and error" methods: an arrangement has been proposed, the intensities of X-ray reflections it would give have been calculated, and these calculated intensities have been compared with the measured intensities; if they were wrong, another arrangement was tried, and so on until a good match between calculated and measured intensities was obtained. But the trial arrangements are never selected blindly; for, as we have seen in earlier chapters, a good deal of information about the internal symmetry of a crystal can be obtained from its shape; the shape indicates that the internal arrangement must possess certain symmetries and lack others.

The shape symmetry limits the number of possible arrangements, but the choice may still be embarrassingly large; in the most symmetrical class of the orthorhombic system, for instance, there are twenty-two space groups. The correct one can often be deduced by looking at the array of X-ray reflections to see first of all what symmetries it shows, and then to see which reflections are there and which ones are missing—for it is very often found that not all the possible reflections are produced: some are missing, and if there is a systematic pattern of absences, this is an important clue to the internal symmetries.

It works in this way. Molecules in crystals are more often than not related to each other by symmetry elements involving translation—the screw axes and glide planes described in the preceding chapter. The significant point about twofold screw axes and glide planes, where X-ray reflections are concerned, is that along the screw axis or the glide direction, the repeating groups of atoms are interleaved at exactly halfway by equivalent groups as in Fig. 118. The result is that when X-rays are reflected by planes A and B, with the waves from B exactly one wavelength behind those from A (which means, exactly in step) then the waves from the interleaving planes X and Y are exactly half

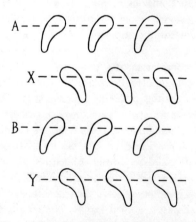

Fig. 118. To explain why certain reflections are missing when the structure has symmetry elements involving translation.

a wavelength out of step (that is, exactly opposite in phase, with troughs matching crests), and being of the same strength, exactly cancel the others. The interleaving groups are not oriented in the same way as the reference groups, but this does not matter; if they are halfway between, cancellation of waves is inevitable. The X-ray reflection that would otherwise be expected is therefore missing. It is in this manner that all symmetry elements involving translation can be detected: the translation causes certain reflections to be missing. Glide planes cut out more reflections than twofold screw axes; and naturally threefold, fourfold and sixfold screw axes, with their interleavings at intervals of one-third, one-fourth and one-sixth of the full repeat distance, each lead to characteristic sets of missing reflections.

In short, by surveying the X-ray diffraction pattern for symmetries and missing reflections, it is often possible to settle which combination of symmetry elements—which space group —the arrangement inside the crystal possesses. This is an immense help, for it settles *how* the molecules are arranged. But there is still a long way to go, for it is still necessary to find out the shape of the molecules, how they are tilted with respect to each other and how far apart they are. In the early days of the subject, this had to be done by putting atoms in likely positions, calculating the intensities of the reflections which would be given by this set of positions, and comparing them with the measured intensities. It is still necessary to do this for some structures; but with the growth of experience of many different types of molecules, the distances between atoms and the angles between their bonds are known, and for some types of molecules which are expected to be rigid, there is from the start little doubt about the shape and dimensions, and it is only necessary to make trials of different tilts and different clearance distances.

Other types of molecules are not rigid; chain molecules, for instance, can assume various shapes—simple zigzags, helices of various sorts, and meandering forms. The structural problem is therefore more difficult, but again the accumulation of experience makes it possible to attempt the solution of structures which

at one time would have seemed to be of forbidding difficulty.
Moreover, many ingenious methods, some mathematical and
others experimental, have been devised which may either give
clues to the shapes of the molecules or else settle the phases of
some of the diffracted waves. The crystallographer now has a
battery of methods which he can try in appropriate circumstances
and which may take him a little nearer to his goal—though none
of them has the power and certainty of the "heavy atom" method.
In tackling a new type of structure, the crystallographer's hope
is that this crystal will contain a heavy atom favourably placed
to dominate the phases—or that by chemical means he can put
one in without wrecking the structure.

Some of these methods are too technical to be described here;
but there is one group of methods that can be illustrated without
any great technicalities, and which indeed are very instructive
as well as elegant, and help to make clear the relations between
patterns and their diffraction effects. They are methods that use
optical diffraction as a faithful analogy of X-ray diffraction; they
are indeed, in principle, elaborations of the handkerchief experiment mentioned earlier as the simplest demonstration of the
phenomenon of diffraction. If you look through a handkerchief
at a distant point of monochromatic light, you see an array of
points of light, in a square formation. As far as the light rays
are concerned, a handkerchief is a regular array of holes in a
square formation; interference effects cause the light waves to
be cancelled in some directions and reinforced in others, and the
directions of reinforcement are in a square formation simply
because the holes are in a square formation. Notice that the
intensities fade off gradually with increasing distance from the
center. But what happens if we use a more elaborate pattern of
holes—if the pattern unit is not a single hole as in the handkerchief, but a group of holes arranged like a group of atoms in a
molecule? The answer is that the diffraction pattern that is
seen on looking through the hole pattern will again consist of
an array of points of light arranged in a square formation, but
the intensities of the points of light are all different—they vary
greatly from one to the next.

An example is shown in Plate 12. The upper photograph is the (much magnified) pattern of holes, in which each pattern-unit is a group of holes; they are not precisely holes, but more or less clear spots in an otherwise black photographic plate—for this tiny repeating pattern (with a unit cell $\frac{1}{5}$ millimeter square) was made by a photographic multiplication and reduction process. The lower photograph is the diffraction pattern which is seen on looking through the hole pattern at a monochromatic point of light. (This again is much magnified.) The points of light are in a square formation because the pattern has a square unit cell; the intensities vary greatly from one to the next, and—this is the important point—these intensities depend on the details of the pattern unit.

The pattern in the upper photograph is an imitation of a crystal structure; the holes are arranged in precisely the same manner as the atoms in the crystal structure of phthalocyanine as seen in one particular direction; this is the same molecule as in Fig. 117 except that there is no heavy metal atom in the center of it; the molecules of this metal-free phthalocyanine are tilted somewhat differently from those of the platinum compound shown in Fig. 117, but the identical formation of interlinked rings of atoms is clear. The usefulness of the imitation lies in the fact that in the diffraction pattern of it in the lower photograph, the variation of intensity from one spot to the next corresponds faithfully to the variation of intensity in the X-ray diffraction pattern given by the real crystal (for this particular view of the crystal).

Diffraction experiments of this sort, using visible light instead of X-rays and artificially constructed patterns instead of real crystals, are useful in two ways. They can be used in place of calculations, for testing whether particular arrangements of atoms give the right intensities in the diffraction patterns; if one arrangement gives wrong intensities, others can be tried easily —for the patterns can be made quite quickly. But they are also useful in a more general way; by making all sorts of arrangements and examining their diffraction patterns, the investigator can learn a lot about the relation between an arrangement and its diffraction effects, and in fact as a result of such experiments, it is now sometimes possible to infer the presence of a particular group of atoms or form of molecule from the general character- istics of the X-ray diffraction pattern, and to deduce its orienta- tion in the unit cell—just by looking at the diffraction pattern. Deductions made in this way have to be followed up by calcula- tions to fill in the details and improve the accuracy, but the first rough idea, which is often the most difficult stage in the solu- tion of the puzzle, is sometimes achieved by the optical methods or by making use of the lessons that have been learned by optical experiments.

These lessons may be described crudely as lessons in turning things inside out. There is always an inside-out relation between an arrangement and the diffraction pattern given by it. We have seen that the smaller the spacing between the units of a pattern, the more spread out is the diffraction pattern. Another aspect of the inside out relation is this: in a crystal the pattern units in the array are *all the same* but each pattern-unit may be complex in detail, whereas in the diffraction pattern the characteristics are reversed—the spots are all *different* (in intensity) but each spot has no detailed structure.

Over the years, the structures of many different crystals have been discovered by the use of all sorts of methods. As an intellectual exercise, it is a great game, far more satisfying than solving crossword puzzles or the other types of superficial puzzles that are invented for our amusement. But of course there is far more to it than that; the motives for attempting to solve the structures of the crystalline substances that are found in nature or are made for our use go very deep into natural philosophy. First of all there is what might be called sheer curiosity to know how the various crystals are constructed; "sheer curiosity" may sound superficial, but in fact it means fascination by the structure of the world we live in, and is really a profoundly religious attitude. With the accumulation of knowledge, it becomes possible to trace general principles of structure—to see how certain types of arrangement come about as the result of the relative sizes of atoms and the forces between them; in this way, the subject of mineralogy has been immensely developed and indeed largely rewritten; the reasons for many of the complexities of composition which at one time seemed capricious are now clear—there is often a geometrical rather than a chemical basis for them.

The increasing accuracy with which atomic positions can be pinpointed has led to precise determinations of the distances between chemically joined atoms and of the angles between the bonds, and crystallography has in this way come to play an important part in the development of deep-seated theories of chemical bonding—for the distances and angles are bound up with the electronic forces that are responsible for chemical bonding.

The development of methods of helping to solve complex structures has been such that it is now sometimes possible to solve structures even when the chemical constitution is incompletely known: by finding the positions of the atoms in the crystal, the crystallographer can find out which ones are joined together (the distances between joined atoms are much smaller than those between atoms that are not joined), and in this way he can fill in awkward gaps in chemical knowledge. It will be evident from what I have said earlier that for molecules containing a heavy atom to dominate the phases of the diffracted X-rays, there is no insuperable difficulty in this; there is much hard work, but there is no puzzle-solving; one need know nothing about the linking of the atoms—it will all come out in the contour map which is the result of the calculations. The prospects are more dubious when there is no heavy atom; or when (as sometimes happens) heavy atoms are in unsuitable positions in the structure; nevertheless, a many-pronged approach which uses all the available methods and experience is often successful. Outstanding examples have been the structures of penicillin and vitamin B_{12}.

Penicillin, a substance extracted from a particular kind of mold, has been spectacularly successful in the treatment of various diseases; chemically it is a most unusual type of molecule, and although the linking of most of the atoms was established by the methods of the organic chemist which involve breaking down the molecule and identifying the fragments, there was a doubt about the linking in one part of the molecule. The solution of the crystal structures of two of its salts settled the problem and showed the presence of a very unusual ring system. For neither of these crystals were the phase-dominating methods very helpful; in the sodium salt no atom was heavy enough, and in the rubidium salt the heavy rubidium atoms were found to be in unsuitable positions in which they only dominated *some* of the phases. However, by using most of the resources known at the time, including the optical imitation methods, and comparing the evidence from the two quite different crystal structures, the problem was solved. It involved finding the general shape of the molecule, which turned out to be quite different from the first suggestions, and pinpointing the positions of twenty-four atoms. The molecule is illustrated in Fig. 119; the unusual ring system is the four-atom ring in the center part of the molecule; suggestions based on admittedly shaky chemical evidence had favoured a quite different linking in this part of the molecule.

Vitamin B_{12}, a substance present in liver, is a much more complex substance than penicillin. It had been known for a long time that there is a substance in liver that is valuable for the treatment of pernicious anaemia; when at last it was extracted and isolated, it was found to consist of very complex molecules containing about 100 atoms (not counting hydrogens); it forms red crystals which give very detailed X-ray diffraction patterns. Chemical evidence had shown that all sorts of different groups of atoms were present, but far less of the chemical structure was known than in the case of penicillin. One unusual feature is the presence of a cobalt atom; this atom, though heavier than any of the others in the molecule, is not heavy enough to dominate all the phases and make possible a straightforward calculation of the structure; nevertheless, its presence gave some valuable clues, and by following these up and patiently adding more and more detail, partly by hard work and partly by the inspired guessing born of experience, Dorothy Hodgkin and her collaborators at

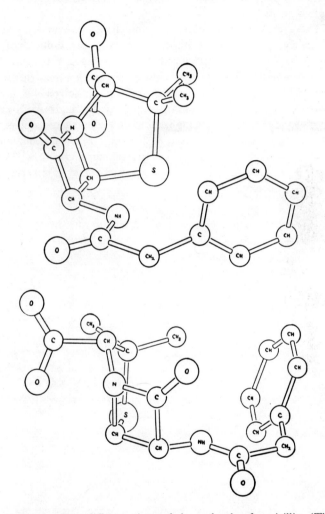

Fig. 119. Two different views of the molecule of penicillin. (The arrangement of molecules in the crystal of the sodium salt is illustrated in Fig. 108.)

Oxford were able eventually to reveal the whole complex molecule in all its detail.

These are examples of structures which have been solved without very much help from the heavy-atom phase-dominating methods. But when sufficiently heavy atoms *are* present in suitable positions, or can be put in without wrecking the structure, very much more complex structures can be solved—in fact, there is in principle no limit, and these methods of X-ray crystallography are now being used to find the structures of very complex substances which are of the most profound and far-reaching significance in the chemistry of living creatures. This work is of such magnitude and importance that it deserves a chapter to itself.

CHAPTER 14

The Crystals of the
Chains of Life

Among the thousands of different substances which take part in the chemistry of living creatures, certain types stand out as being of special importance: they occupy key positions in the scheme of organization, because of their role in the structure of the cells and tissues, or because they control vital chemical processes, or because they are concerned with the way in which particular characteristics are passed on from parents to children. The two great classes of substances which have these important functions are known as proteins and the salts of nucleic acids (sodium salts, for the most part). Proteins form a substantial proportion of the weight of animal tissues, and have a variety of functions: some of them appear to control chemical processes in the cells, others constitute muscles and tendons and so control movements, while others appear as hair on mammals or feathers on birds; they all have the same sort of chemical structure, though they differ in detail. Salts of nucleic acids (nucleates) are the substances in cell nuclei which are responsible for the transmission of individual characteristics from parents to children; they are quite different chemically from proteins, but the nucleates in different species are very similar to each other, though again differing in detail.

The molecules of both these classes of substances are very large; they contain thousands of atoms and are of great chemical complexity, as we might expect in view of the very specialized roles they play in living organisms. The two are quite different chemically but they have one feature in common—in both types of substances the main feature of the molecular structure is a very long chain of atoms; there are side groups, some of which are short chains, but the main feature is the very long central chain of hundreds or thousands of atoms. Why the chain form?

No doubt these molecules have to be large and complex because they have special and complex jobs to do, but other types of large complex molecules can be imagined—cage structures, and two- or three-dimensional networks, for instance. Long chain molecules of a simpler type are becoming familiar nowadays, in plastics, synthetic fibers, and rubbers, and the properties of these substances suggest the reason why some of the proteins have long chain molecules—for it is this type of molecule that gives a combination of strength with flexibility, and these qualities are certainly necessary in muscles and tendons, as well as in hair and wool. For the other key substances that control the chemical processes in the living cell, including the chemistry of heredity, the reasons for the chain character are probably more subtle, but flexibility appears to play an important part here too, as we shall see—and flexibility is the outstanding characteristic of the chain type of molecule: other large complex types would be too rigid, and their active chemical groups would be less accessible.

In both types of key substances the main chains have a quite regular structure, with a particular sequence of atoms repeated over and over again along the whole length of the chain. In this respect they are like the much simpler long-chain substances we use as plastics and synthetic fibers; but the chains of life differ from our synthetic chains by having a complex succession of different side groups. In the proteins, for instance, the main chain consists of many repetitions of a three-atom group, a nitrogen atom followed by two carbon atoms (see Fig. 120);

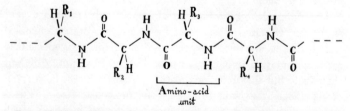

Fig. 120. A small part of a protein molecule, in the plane zigzag conformation which is found in silk and certain other proteins. (Heavily marked links are in front of the zigzag plane, lightly marked links are behind.)

the nitrogen always carries a hydrogen atom, one of the carbon atoms always carries an oxygen atom, while the other carbon atom always carries one hydrogen atom and one side group— and this is where the complexity comes in, for there are twenty different side groups, and any one protein has a particular succession of side groups. In Fig. 120 the side groups are represented by the symbols R_1, R_2, R_3, ...; each consists of a few atoms, sometimes in rings or short chains, and always restricted to the atoms carbon, nitrogen, oxygen, hydrogen, and sulfur. The complete unit which includes three chain atoms and one side group is known as an amino acid unit.

This knowledge of the structure of protein molecules has been obtained by chemical methods, which consist of breaking the molecule into fragments by known chemical reactions and identifying the fragments. Organic chemistry consists of a vast accumulation of experience about which substances and what conditions are necessary to make or break particular bonds or replace one group of atoms by another; and by the carefully controlled breakdown of protein molecules into pieces containing two, three, or more side groups—pieces which can be identified because the substances have been synthesized—it has been found possible by a prodigious amount of work to establish the complete succession of side groups in certain proteins, notably insulin, the substance extracted from the pancreas of animals which is vitally important in the control of diabetes. In most proteins, however, the succession is still unknown; the *proportions* of the different side groups are known, for it is relatively easy to break down the chain into individual units and analyze the amounts, but there is only fragmentary knowledge of the *succession*.

As the power of X-ray diffraction methods to discover the structure of crystals grew, some of the more adventurous crystallographers turned their attention to proteins—first of all to the ones which are found to be already in imperfect crystalline arrangement. These are the proteins in hair and in muscles. W. T. Astbury of Leeds University, in his pioneer work on these substances, studied their X-ray diffraction patterns and

concluded, first, that the chain molecules are in a fairly extended
form (certainly not curled up in balls), and second, that by
stretching in steam, it is possible to pull them out to a fully
extended form—a convincing demonstration of the flexibility of
the molecules. This does not mean that the chain is a straight
line; the utmost extension possible is to the zigzag form of
Fig. 120, because powerful forces in the molecules insist on
keeping the angles between the bonds to about 110°; this is
consistent with what we know of other chain substances like
polythene and nylon. The less extended form of the unstretched
molecules is attained, not by altering the bond angles, but by
using the bonds as swivelling joints; all sorts of curled-up
configurations could be attained in this way without altering the
bond angles at all. The precise conformation has been the subject
of much speculation but it now seems pretty certain that the
molecules have the general form of a helix, as shown in Fig. 121.
The precise dimensions of this helix were first suggested by
Linus Pauling of the California Institute of Technology, but the
evidence for it is based on the interpretation of X-ray diffraction
patterns in the light of our deepening understanding of the
relation of diffraction effects to atomic patterns which has come
about by mathematical and optical studies.

Why do these chain molecules take up a helical form rather
than a simple folded form? This question will take us back to
the asymmetric molecules discussed in Chapter 11—for one of
the outstanding facts about protein molecules is that each
amino acid unit of the chain (three chain atoms plus the associated
side group) is asymmetric. Like so many of the substances in
living creatures, protein molecules are one-handed, and all the
twenty different types of amino acid units found in the proteins
of all living creatures are one-handed, all in the same sense.
It is scarcely possible to imagine a more striking piece of evidence
for the unity of all life on earth; it presumably dates back to
the first asymmetric molecules, which for some unknown reason
were of one hand; the whole process of evolution took a stereochemically one-handed course. Now a chain composed of
asymmetric units, if it does curl up, is likely to curl in one

direction rather than the other: the side groups push the main chain in one direction rather than the other. Since all the side groups have the same configuration, they all push the main chain in the same direction, and this leads to a helical form. The direction of twist in the extended-chain proteins has not been ascertained experimentally, but it can hardly be different from that which *has* been found in some other proteins, as we shall see later—and this is a *right-handed screw*. We are all completely committed, stereochemically speaking, to a right-handed existence.

The reason for the particular helix in Fig. 121—for that particular amount of curl—is also clear: it allows an NH group

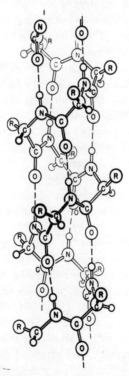

FIG. 121. The helical form assumed by some protein molecules. The broken lines represent the electrostatic attractions known as "hydrogen bonds."

of one part of the molecule to get close to a CO group further along the chain. There is a strong attraction between the positively charged hydrogen atom of an NH group and the negatively charged oxygen atom of a CO group, of the same nature as the strong attractions that hold sugar molecules together in the crystal—but here in the proteins it holds different parts of the same molecule together, one turn of the coil to the next turn. This attraction (the "hydrogen bond"), which had already been recognized in crystals of other chain molecules (in nylon, for instance, it holds neighboring molecules together), was indeed the basis of Pauling's suggestion of this particular helix.

Not all the fibrous proteins have their molecules curled into this helical form. In the fibers of natural silk—the threads spun by the silkworm—the protein molecules, which are arranged in crystalline form, are nearly fully extended, having nearly the plane zigzag form of Fig. 120. Whether a molecule is nearly fully extended or curled into a shorter helical form depends on which side groups are there; although twenty different amino acids are known as constituents of protein molecules, not all are present in any one protein; some proteins have only a few different ones, and the silk protein consists mostly of two of the simplest (having the smallest side groups). This is no doubt why it is able to stay nearly fully extended: its small side groups do not push it into a curled form. Another example is collagen, the protein of animal tendons; its molecules adopt the fairly extended form of a slowly turning helix, and three of them twist around each other like a slightly twisted rope, being held strongly together by hydrogen bonds. The shape of this molecule is influenced by the fact that something like one-third of its amino acid units are of one special type which imposes a special conformation on the chain.

These are the fibrous proteins—the ones that are already in partly crystalline form with chains lying along the fiber direction in hair, muscle, or tendon, and arranged either parallel to each other or twisted together, as befits their fibrous character and their functions in living creatures. They are like the synthetic fibers nylon and "Terylene," which also have extended chains packed together with crystalline regularity. They are not completely crystalline, but only partly so; in some places the chains are arranged with precise crystalline regularity, but in others they are disordered, and this partly crystalline texture (Fig. 122), with crystals woven together by molecules passing through both crystalline and disordered regions, is believed to be responsible for their useful combination of flexibility and strength.

The proteins which have chemical rather than structural functions are not in crystalline form in living creatures. They are mixed with other substances in cells and tissues, and not arranged in an ordered way; probably they need to be free and accessible to fulfil their chemical functions. They also differ from the structural proteins in another way: their molecules are not in extended form but are curled up into balls; this has been

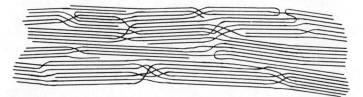

FIG. 122. The molecular texture in fibrous substances. The lines represent chain molecules, which in some places are packed parallel, with crystalline regularity, and in others are disordered. The disordered regions confer flexibility.

known for some time as a result of studies of their behavior in solution. Fortunately some of them can be crystallized if they are carefully separated from other substances and given the chance to form an ordered arrangement. I say "fortunately" because the existence of crystals affords an opportunity of studying the structure of the molecules to a degree of detail that would otherwise be out of the question. A crystal, in which the molecules are oriented precisely and lined up in ranks, acts as a vastly enlarged model of a molecule or a small group of molecules. Just because all the molecules act together in X-ray diffraction, for instance, they give detailed information which could never be obtained from isolated or disarranged molecules. Some of the proteins crystallize with a degree of perfection that may seem surprising for such flexible molecules; they give X-ray diffraction patterns with thousands of reflections, providing enough evidence to give a detailed picture of the structure and the arrangement of the molecules, if only the immensely difficult problems of interpretation can be solved.

In the thirties of this century a few crystallographers began to study some of these crystals, notably insulin, the substance which is used in the treatment of diabetes, and hemoglobin, the substance in red blood corpuscles which performs the vital function of combining with oxygen from the air and carrying it through blood vessels to different parts of the body. (Hemoglobin crystals are depicted in Fig. 123.) They experimented with

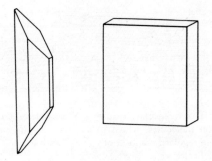

Fig. 123.   Two different types of hemoglobin crystals. Proteins often crystallize in two or more different forms, in which the molecules are arranged in different ways. The crystallographer interested in the structure of the molecule selects the type most suitable for detailed study.

different methods of growing suitable crystals for X-ray studies, and with methods of getting the best possible X-ray patterns from crystals kept in contact with liquids of the right composition (an essential condition for the preservation of a high degree of regularity). Although these crystals were of a complexity very far beyond that of any structures hitherto solved, the fascination of their key role in the chemistry of living creatures impelled crystallographers toward attempts at solving the structural problems. A detailed solution would give more than one type of valuable information. In the first place, it would give the order of succession of the different amino acid units along the chain, which was at that time not known for any protein molecule; secondly, it would give the manner in which the long chain molecule is curled up, and this seems to be just as important for the biochemical functioning of the molecule as the chemical linking.

The first stages in the interpretation of the X-ray diffraction patterns were straightforward: for several proteins the size and shape of the unit cell, the space group symmetry, and the general over-all shape of the molecule were found without much diffi-culty. To get any further it was, as usual, necessary to solve the phase problem; and the best way of doing this is, as we have seen in the previous chapter, to use a crystal which has heavy atoms in suitable positions, to dominate the phases of the X-ray reflec-tions. Hemoglobin does contain an iron atom (in the part of the molecule which combines with oxygen), but this in itself is quite inadequate, for various reasons. Before methods of attaching heavy atoms to the molecules were discovered, the investigators tried all sorts of ingenious methods of trying to get round the phase problem—with only very limited success, for twenty years. Eventually it was found possible to attach heavy atoms like mercury and silver to the molecules of two proteins, hemoglobin and myoglobin, without altering the crystal structures in any essential way, and this opened the way to detailed solutions of the structural problems.

Even then it was not all plain sailing. Far from it: there were still some difficult problems to solve. In crystals as complex as these, composed of molecules containing thousands of atoms, no one heavy atom can really dominate the phases of the X-ray reflections. Nevertheless, in the circumstances it is possible to use another procedure which does not rely on domination: when there are two crystals of the same structure, one with and the other without a heavy atom, the differences of intensity between corresponding X-ray reflections from the two crystals

indicate the phases; it depends on whether the reflection from
the heavy-atom crystal is stronger or weaker than that from the
crystal without the heavy atom. So far, so good; but the method
only works when it is simply a question of deciding whether the
waves have a crest or a trough exactly at the unit cell corner
—and this is so only for *some* of the reflections of these crystals.
For many of the reflections it is not as simple as this; protein
crystals do not have a center of symmetry, and this means that
for many of the reflections the waves can have *any* relation to
the unit cell corner, with fractional phase displacements. To
cut a long story short, this difficulty was dealt with by putting
in a different heavy atom, which forturately went into a different
place in the crystal; in these circumstances the fractional phase
displacements can be worked out. In actual fact several different
crystals were made, all with the same essential structure, with
heavy atoms in several different positions; by combining the
evidence from them, greater accuracy was obtained.

These methods were developed by Max Perutz and John
Kendrew at Cambridge, and were first applied to the two proteins
hemoglobin and myoglobin. Success came first for myoglobin;
this is the substance that colors the muscles of vertebrate
mammals red. It has two virtues from the X-ray crystallographer's
point of view: its molecules are only one-quarter the size of
hemoglobin molecules (but even so, contain 153 amino acid
units, each consisting of a number of atoms), and its X-ray
diffraction patterns are so detailed that it is possible in principle
to carry the interpretation to the pinpointing of individual atoms;
for hemoglobin and some other proteins it will not be possible
to go as far as this. The work on myoglobin involved measurements of the intensities of thousands of X-ray reflections for
each of the heavy-atom-containing crystals as well as the original
protein; then followed some comprehensive calculations to get
the figures for the different crystals on the same scale and to
find the relative positions of the heavy atoms in the different
crystals, further calculations to arrive at the phase relations for
all the thousands of reflections, and finally the colossal calculation
of the image of the structure. The calculations were done on an

electronic computer; the work would have been quite impracticable otherwise. The first result was an image of the crystal structure which showed for the first time the general architecture of a protein molecule—the twists and turns of the chain to form a compact ball, and the position of the iron-containing heme group which is responsible for the oxygen-carrying function of the molecule. A photograph of a model of the molecule is shown in Plate 13. It is folded up in a quite irregular way.

Further work along the same lines, in which still more X-ray reflections were included in the calculations, revealed the detailed structure of the chain, which shows in the straight portions the very type of helix that had been suggested some years earlier by Pauling; it shows also that the helix is a right-hand screw. (This is the basis for the statement made earlier in this chapter, that we are all committed to a stereochemically right-handed existence— for all the amino acid units in all the proteins are of the same hand, and would impose the same right-handed screw twist on other protein chains.) Where the chain turns a corner, the conformation is not helical. Why it turns corners is not clear yet, for the amino acid units have not all been identified at the time of writing; this is an important question, because the general shape of the whole molecule presumably depends on the exact sequence of amino acid units.

The hemoglobin molecule is four times the size of the myoglobin molecule and consists of four chains associated together. The analysis of its crystal structure has not been carried to the same fineness of detail as that of myoglobin—indeed there is not enough X-ray information to make it possible to go as far—but the first stage of analysis, to the point of showing the general conformation of the chains, has revealed that the whole molecule is in four sections, each corresponding closely to the myoglobin molecule in the twists and turns of the chain and the position of the heme group. The four sections of the hemoglobin molecule are not all the same—they are in two pairs, differing a little from each other and from the myoglobin molecule; but the general design is essentially the same throughout. Such a striking correspondence is the best possible guarantee of the authenticity

of the results for both substances, and a wonderful demonstration
that these protein molecules having similar functions are built
according to the same general plan. Moreover, the myoglobins
and hemoglobins of different species of vertebrates resemble
each other closely. The first X-ray work was done on myoglobin
from the sperm whale and hemoglobin from the horse; but it has
since been found that the molecules of seal myoglobin and bovine
hemoglobin have the same general form, though there are minor
differences in chemical composition.

Does the conformation of a protein molecule in the crystal
correspond to the conformation of the free molecule in solution
in physiological conditions? It is known that the general shapes
correspond, and although there is evidence of a certain amount
of change when the composition of the solution changes (as
might be expected of such flexible molecules), the indications
are that the structure in the crystal is closely related to that of
the molecule when it is doing its job in a living creature. How
much light will be thrown on these functions by our new knowledge of protein structure remains to be seen. There are many
baffling problems. For instance, the oxygen-carrying function
of hemoglobin and myoglobin is based on the heme group,
which is an iron-containing group quite different from the
amino acid chain which makes up the rest of the molecule. It
is not known why the heme group should have an enormous
curled-up amino acid chain attached to it at all. Yet the amino
acid chain does play a vital part in the process, for the heme
group does not work without it, and if it does not contain exactly
the right sequence of amino acid units, the consequences are
serious: there are certain congenital blood defects in human
beings, having the most serious consequences for the unfortunate
individuals in which they occur, which are due to a change of
just one amino acid unit in the 300 or so in a half-molecule of
hemoglobin. This is one of the things about which we may gain a
valuable understanding; but there are many more, and the prospects are such that the achievement of discovering the structure
and conformation of protein molecules may well be said to be the
biggest thing that has happened yet in X-ray crystallography

and one of the outstanding scientific achievements of this century. Crystals were first studied for their own sake, but the results of the investigations spread far and wide into other branches of knowledge.

If the proteins can be said to occupy a variety of key positions in the chemistry of living creatures, the nucleates may fairly be described as being central in the whole scheme, for these are the substances which appear to control protein synthesis and the transmission of inherited characteristics from parents to children. The proteins appear to control the chemical and mechanical functioning of the living organism, but they are themselves controlled by the nucleates: these are the implications of recent biochemical research. It has been recognized for many years that in the nucleus of each living cell is a collection of little things called chromosomes, the number and shape of which is characteristic of the species. They are in pairs, and a man has 23 pairs, a cat 19, a mouse 20, and a horse 30 pairs. (The name "chromosome" means "colored body"; they are not naturally colored, but can absorb certain dyes, and are shown up under the microscope in this way.) They are often rod-shaped, and a great amount of evidence, based on much patient experiment and observation, has shown that particular inherited characters like eye color are associated with minute regions arranged in a line along the rod-shaped chromosome. These regions are called "genes." Chemically the chromosomes of all species consist of nucleate—a particular type called deoxyribonucleate or DNA— and protein, and for certain organisms it has been proved that the DNA is the carrier of the cell's inheritance. In the rest of the cell is a slightly different type of nucleate—ribonucleate or RNA—which appears to control protein synthesis, and may well be the template on which the protein molecule is assembled. It has not been proved that they have these functions in all living organisms, but it begins to appear likely.

Nucleates (salts of nucleic acids) can be isolated by careful chemical separation methods, and a good deal has been learned about them. Their molecules, like those of the proteins, consist of very long chains, but in chemical composition the two are

completely different. The long chain of a DNA molecule is a
string of alternate phosphoric acid and sugar groups, and attached
to each sugar group is a side group, represented in Fig. 124 by
A, *C*, *T*, and *G*. The sodium (or other) ions are not specifically
attached, but are located near the phosphoric acid groups. There
are only four different kinds of side groups in the DNA from
different species; the same four occur in the DNA from various
living species, though in different proportions. (The letters *A*,
C, *T*, and *G* are the initial letters of the chemical names of the
side groups.) In RNA the sugar group is slightly different, and
another side group *U* takes the place of *T*. There is a contrast
here with the proteins, in which twenty different side groups
are known, and occur in various combinations and proportions
in different species, providing an immense range of variation in
sequence and proportion. It is somewhat surprising to find that
nucleates have only four different side groups, for the indications
are that they have functions which demand a vast range of

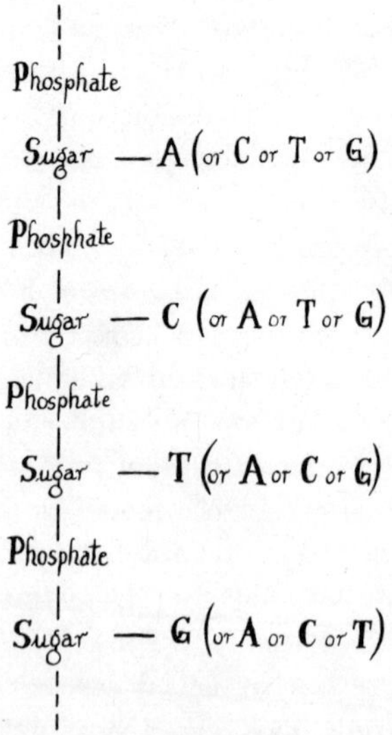

Phosphate

Sugar — A (or C or T or G)

Phosphate

Sugar — C (or A or T or G)

Phosphate

Sugar — T (or A or C or G)

Phosphate

Sugar — G (or A or C or T)

FIG. 124.   A small part of a DNA molecule. The order of succession
of the four different side groups is not known.

variation: if they are responsible for the differences between species and between the individuals of each species, and control the synthesis of the proteins required to give material expression of these variations, how do they do it with apparently such meager resources?

The beginning of a possible answer to this question can be given. Although there are only four different side groups, the chains are immensely long, containing thousands of units, and if the secret is in the sequence of side chains, it it possible to imagine very large numbers of different sequences in a chain of this great length. If nucleates control protein synthesis, what they have to do is to join twenty different types of amino acid units together in the right sequence; it has been found that if it is supposed that a particular sequence of three nucleate side groups specifies that one particular amino acid unit is required at that point, then it is possible to have twenty different triplets (*ATA*, *TCA*, *TGC*, *ACC*, and so on) to specify which of the twenty amino acid units is to come next. A particular sequence of triplets would therefore specify a whole long protein molecule. This is speculation, but it does show in principle that it is not impossible to get the necessary complexity, even though there are only four different nucleate side groups. But how does it work? It is very difficult to envisage a definite geometry and chemistry for this template assembly line.

Confronted by such an intriguing problem, it is not surprising that scientists use all the methods they can think of to gather information about the geometry of nucleate molecules. Naturally they have tried X-ray diffraction, owing to its success in other fields; and the results, though much more limited than in the case of the proteins, have played a part in the development of recent ideas. The prospects as we have seen, depend on the extent to which the molecules arrange themselves in an orderly crystalline pattern. Nucleate molecules in living cells are not curled up in balls, though at certain stages they are folded up in the chromosomes. When extracted, they do crystallize to some extent by arranging themselves side by side, but the perfection falls short of that found in the globular proteins, and single crystals have not been obtained. Investigators have had to do the best they could with fibre specimens made by drawing threads of the material in much the same way as synthetic fibers of nylon are made; and the X-ray patterns given by these fibers are far less detailed than those given by the globular proteins. Nevertheless, studies of these patterns have suggested the general form of the molecules in one type of nucleate crystal—once more a helical form—and moreover have indicated its dimensions and hinted that there are two helices intertwined.

Partly on the basis of evidence of this sort, and partly for other reasons, a possible model of the DNA structure has been suggested by J. D. Watson and F. H. C. Crick which could at any rate explain how DNA molecules reproduce *themselves*—which of course they must do, in addition to their other tasks. The first essential feature of this model is a pair of chains, linked together by attractions between the side chains; these attractions are those same "hydrogen bonds" that bind nylon molecules together and knit the successive coils of the protein chain together. A further important feature is based on the fact that although the proportions of the four side groups A, C, T, and G vary in different species, the amount of A is always equal to that of T, and the amount of C is always equal to that of G; it is therefore suggested that A on one chain is always linked to T of the other, and that C is always linked to G. (Scale models of the molecules show that this is reasonable.) Moreover, the two chains run in opposite directions; they are complementary in every sense; they are identical chains which fit together when one is reversed (Fig. 125). To complete the picture, the two chains are twined together to form the double helix shown in Fig. 126, which looks like a helical staircase with the linked side groups forming the steps. The details are based on known interatomic distances, and the general form fits in with the X-ray patterns.

Whether the helical form plays an essential part in the functioning is not clear; but the structure of two linked complementary chains provides a very plausible self-replicating mechanism—for if the two chains come apart, and a new chain forms on each (being assembled from small-molecule ingredients in the cell), the new chains are bound to have the right structure, if the idea that A links to T and C to G is right; each free chain acts as the template for the formation of a new chain, which curls around the old one to make a new double helix. Some ingenious experiments have given good reason to believe that this self-replicating mechanism based on the idea of a pair of linked complementary chains is correct in principle; so it can be said that in a broad general way we do understand how DNA molecules can reproduce themselves according to the very specific and complex pattern of succession which is necessary to transmit hereditary characteristics.

FIG. 125. Two identical DNA chains, reversed and complementary, fitting together.

This is all very well in a general way, but to get any further it will be necessary to put more detail into the picture, first by finding the succession of A, C, T, and G units in DNA molecules, and second by studying the association of nucleate and protein molecules. To find the succession of units in nucleate molecules, attempts are naturally being made by both chemical and X-ray methods; perhaps by a combination of the two the success attained for one of the proteins may be repeated for one of the nucleates. For X-ray methods the prospects depend very much on how well nucleates can be persuaded to crystallize. If they crystallized as well as the globular proteins it might be

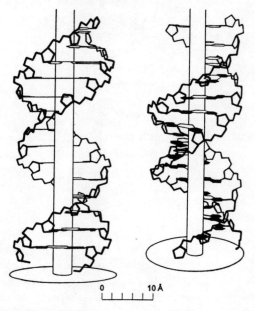

0   10 Å

FIG. 126.   The double helical structure for DNA, suggested by Watson and Crick.

possible to obtain information on the succession of units, similar to that which has been obtained for myoglobin; but so far the crystals obtained, and the X-ray patterns from them, fall far short of this standard.

The association of nucleate and protein molecules is very difficult to study in the higher organisms, but some of the very simple organisms called viruses seem to consist of nothing but nucleate and protein, and moreover they crystallize and give X-ray diffraction patterns which indicate a remarkable degree of regularity of structure. As we have already seen, it is the regularity of structure exemplified in crystals that opens out the possibility of obtaining detailed information. Crystallographers have therefore pounced on these substances, as perhaps the simplest examples of the association of nucleic acid and protein that seems to be the chemical key of life.

When a living creature is infected with a virus, what happens is that the virus reproduces itself rapidly, with serious and sometimes disastrous consequences to the infected creature; it seems likely that infection by a virus is the injection of an apparatus for the synthesis of the *wrong* protein—that is why the creature suffers or dies. It has been shown, for some plant viruses, that it is the nucleate, not the protein, that is infective; this has been done by separating the two substances by chemical means, and injecting each separately, with the result that only the nucleate proved to be infective. But to achieve its effects, it manufactures protein—evidently the wrong protein, from the point of view of the infected organism. The point is that the parts played by nucleate and protein appear to be similar in essentials to those in the higher organisms, and it may therefore be justifiable to regard the viruses as models of the life process, reduced to its simplest terms. That is why these substances (or should I call them organisms?) are being studied intensively: it may be possible to learn something from these comparatively simple organisms first, and to work up to the higher organisms later.

Simple they may be in comparison with most living creatures, but in comparison with all the molecules so far mentioned in this book they are exceedingly complicated, or at any rate, very large: for they are many times larger than the protein molecules described a few pages back. They appear to consist of a central core of nucleate surrounded by a coat of protein, and the coat of protein is many times larger than the myoglobin molecules illustrated in Plate 13. However, though they are very large on the molecular scale, the indications of X-ray and electron microscope studies are that there is a surprising regularity of structure: the protein coat surrounding the nucleate core consists of a number of units that are very similar to each other and may even be identical.

The evidence for this statement is that some of the plant viruses are approximately spherical in shape and actually form crystals of cubic symmetry. The formation of crystals having a cubic packing of spheres does not in itself tell us anything about the symmetry of the molecules, for any objects of approximately spherical shape may pack together to give an apparently cubic structure (just because the *are* spherical), even if the internal symmetry of the spherical objects were very low; but the detail in the X-ray diffraction photographs of these crystals is such as to suggest strongly that each spherical virus particle consists of a number of identical subunits, and this has led to the suggestion that a virus particle consists of a core of nucleate (curled up in some unknown manner), to which many identical protein units are attached; we must imagine a central sphere of nucleate (evidently curled up in a ball) having a number of approximately spherical protein units packed together on its surface to form a raspberrylike object.

Electron miscroscope photographs of some viruses of this type do indeed show raspberrylike particles. Plate 14 shows a very striking example; this is an insect virus, a very large molecule indeed, which has a magnificently regular structure. This is displayed more clearly by the model underneath, which is a packing of spheres to form the shape known as an icosahedron— a figure with twenty triangular faces. There is something very interesting about this shape: its symmetry is *not* a crystallographic symmetry, for it has fivefold axes. There is of course no reason why it *should* have a crystallographic symmetry, for this is an isolated object, not a pattern repeating in space. If these particles packed together to form crystals, their fivefold axes would not —in fact, could not—be utilized in the arrangement. In another smaller virus whose shape has not been seen directly in the electron microscope, X-ray diffraction photographs have given strong evidence for the existence of fivefold axes of symmetry in the particles. The essential point is that these shapes with fivefold axes are the natural shapes set up when a number of identical spheres are packed closely, around a central sphere of different radius.

This then is the architecture of these simple organisms: a central core of the nucleate, the self-reproducing substance which is the directing center of the organism, surrounded by a "body" of the simplest possible type—a number of apparently identical protein spheres packed together on the surface.

In another type of virus that has been studied a good deal—tobacco mosaic virus, which is responsible for a disease causing mottling of the leaves of tobacco plants—the particles are long rods, not spheres; and again X-ray diffraction evidence has shown that the nucleate is inside and the protein outside. In this organism it appears that the nucleate is in the form of a helical coil, with protein partly within but mostly outside, forming again a "body" consisting of a number of similar and perhaps identical protein units. (A model is shown in Plate 15.) The dimensions of the inner nucleate helix, the number of protein units to each turn of the outer helix, and the general screw-thread-shape outline are fairly well established, and the X-ray diffraction patterns are sufficiently detailed to promise that much more information can be obtained by further study. Notice again that this particle is not in itself a crystal, but has an internal regularity comparable to that of a crystal.

These long rod-shaped particles do pack together in crystalline array, and the arrangement is hexagonal, as would be expected in the packing of a bundle of sticks. Likewise the spherical viruses pack together, to form, very often, cubic crystals. It is interesting to note that the virus of poliomyelitis (infantile paralysis) has been crystallized, and the shape of the crystals is the familiar rhombic dodecahedron; Fig. 127 shows the crystal shape, together with a model of packed spheres suggesting the probable arrangement of virus particles.

Are viruses living? This is a much debated question, and a very difficult one to answer. They certainly reproduce themselves when they are in suitable surroundings; indeed, in the right plant or animal host they multiply very rapidly, much more rapidly than bacteria. If capacity for self-reproduction is regarded as the criterion of life, then viruses can be said to be living, and virus crystals can fairly be described as living crystals, for crystallized viruses retain their power to infect. The self-reproduction of long chain molecules is not, however, anything radically new from the chemical point of view; it is possible to imagine a mechanism for it in chemical terms, as we have seen in the previous pages. Viruses seem to be entities that are on the borderline between what we would call living and what we would call nonliving. Whether we call them living or not depends on our definition of the word "living." There does not seem to be an utterly radical distinction between what is living and what is not living. Viruses might well be called the "missing link" between living and nonliving matter.

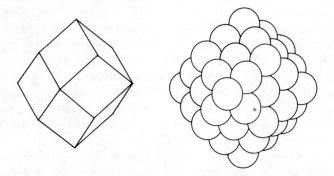

Fig. 127.   A crystal of poliomyelitis virus (a rhombic dodecahedron), with a model of packed spheres suggesting the probable arrangement of virus particles. The arrangement is approximately body-centered cubic, but detailed studies have shown that the unit cell edges are not quite equal in length, and the true symmetry is orthorhombic. The particles, depicted here as spheres, are probably raspberrylike objects, with sixty protein molecules packed around a core of nucleate.

Life seems to be a matter of degree, not of kind; it is not something of a completely new kind added on to matter, but an aspect of the behavior of matter of a particular type which begins to be apparent at a particular degree of complexity of organization. History is repeating itself: at one time it was thought that heat is something *added on* to matter, but it turned out (and it is now universally accepted) that it is nothing more nor less than the *motion* of matter—that it is in fact an aspect of the behavior of matter, not something new or semimaterial, added on. It seems that we are coming to a similar view about life. There is a similar problem about consciousness, which we would all agree is possessed by the "higher" forms of life but does not seem to be possessed by the "lower" forms. It is impossible, however, to draw a sharp dividing line; there is no radical difference, but rather a gradation: again we have to say that it is a matter of degree.

The vague border land between the living and the nonliving which the viruses represent is also the boundary of the crystal kingdom, for these are the most complex substances which crystallize, as far as we know. The capacity to pack in a regular repeating space pattern is common among simpler substances, but higher organisms do not exhibit this type of order.

I said earlier in this book that the shapes and symmetries of crystals are characteristic of "dead" matter: they represent the most primitive kind of internal organization, a monotonous repetition of the same pattern unit in all directions in space. A living organism higher in the scale than a virus consists, not of many identical units, but of a variety of different units, each having its own form and function; so crystalline shape and symmetry in an individual organism are not to be expected. Large numbers of identical organisms could in principle form crystalline arrangements, even if they had an intricate or asymmetric shape; but while something resembling crystalline order can sometimes be discerned in "colonies" of bacteria or in regiments of soldiers, on the whole the individuality of behavior of living organisms prevents the formation of the primitive type or order we call "crystalline." So it is fitting that as we proceed up the scale of complexity, from atoms to simple molecules and then to more and more complex molecules, the last crystals we come to are those of the viruses, which are at the threshold of life. In higher organisms the parts are differentiated in form and function, their shapes and symmetries are of an altogether more subtle type, and the behavior of individuals works against any monotonous repetitive arrangement.

INDEX

283